THE WINE LIST 2006

THE TOP 250 WINES OF THE YEAR
MATTHEW JUKES

headline

To Lucas

Also by Matthew Jukes
THE WINE LIST 2002
THE WINE LIST 2003
THE WINE LIST 2004
THE WINE LIST 2005
AND THE WINE BOOK

Copyright © 2005 Matthew Jukes

www.thewinelist2006.com
www.matthewjukes.com

The right of Matthew Jukes to be identified as the Author of the Work has been asserted by him in accordance with the Copyright, Designs and Patents Act 1988.

First published in 2005 by
HEADLINE BOOK PUBLISHING

1 2

All information regarding recommended prices and availability is correct to the best of the publisher's and author's knowledge at the time of going to press. No responsibility can be taken by the publisher or author if prices or availability change.

A CIP catalogue record for this title is available from the British Library

ISBN 0 7553 1358 5

Printed and bound in the UK by The Bath Press
Designed by Fiona Pike, Pike Design

Headline Book Publishing
A division of Hodder Headline
338 Euston Road
London NW1 3BH

www.headline.co.uk
www.hodderheadline.com

CONTENTS

Welcome back, if you are a season ticket holder, to the number one wine guide in the UK. If you are new to **THE WINE LIST**, I hope you will be able to navigate around the chapters easily. This book will help you find all the wines you need to satiate your thirst, widen your vinous horizons and amaze your taste buds. So, come in, pull up a chair and make yourself at home. All you need is a glass and a corkscrew. Leave the rest to me – sit back, relax and enjoy the ride.

The eagle eyed among you will have spotted the new format – not just the smart new blue livery but also the posh hardback. There are a few other subtle tweaks as well to make it even easier for you to track down the 250 finest wines on the shelves this year.

As usual the book is split into four main sections –

The **Top 250** alone is a decent enough reason to get you out of bed in the morning. This is the definitive distillation of my entire year's tasting notes – including those from my travels all over the world. I ruthlessly cull this collection into the final hard-core 250, taking availability and stockists into play, as well as sheer quality. Fifty-one and a half weeks of non-stop tasting ends and a few days of frantic typing begins!

I am often asked how I decide if a wine is worth listing? The answer is that every one of these wines has scored very highly in my tasting notes. In addition to this they all represent fantastic value for money – whether you are roaming around the £3 mark or orbiting around £50. I have also made sure that every one of these wines is drinking well now – so there is no need to cellar them, just open and wallow. In order to stay ahead of the pack I even taste wines that are not yet bottled. There are sixteen 2005s in this list – they were still on the vine in March! You can read about them before any other people in the UK have even tasted them – and this includes journalists, retailers and, in some cases, even the agents and distributors themselves. I am very lucky to be sent these pre-release samples (thank you winemakers!) and it is invaluable in helping me give you the ultimate selection of wines to choose from. A few of these bottles are in short supply, so if you like the sound of a wine, get on the horn and reserve yourself some stock. Each year a number sell out extremely quickly – you have been warned. Having said that, six months into the life of last year's book, I checked out how many of the wines were available, and was delighted to see that well over two hundred were still going strong. This proves that **THE WINE LIST** is a true annual guide.

Bearing in mind I write every word of this book myself and don't use other people's tasting notes or 'researchers' to do the donkeywork, everything you see is mine. I even update the 250 during the editing and proofing stages to make it as precise as is humanly possible. Every year when The Top 250 is published, wine merchants across the country rush to stock these wines to sell to their clients. Clearly it is too late to list these shops as stockists so, come October, many of these wines will have much wider distribution than is shown here – good news for all. Price-wise, some shops may sell a little over my rrp (which I get from the UK agent), equally others can be cheaper – I note the 'official' list price, so shop around and ask your merchant if they offer case discounts. Remember, if a shop is not on your doorstep, don't let this stop you buying their wines – every single merchant in the Directory delivers nationwide. Last year over a million bottles sported a Top 250 sticker to help you locate them more easily on the shelves. This year the programme is even bigger, so keep your eyes peeled!

So, what trends shone through this year? Last year the New World gained a princely 142 listings. This year they are still up there with 131, dominating the shelves and the centre stage of your dining-room table. Australia and New Zealand combined have a staggering 103 wines – this is a totally awesome result, and fully deserved. If Australia is the mightiest power in the UK wine scene, then New Zealand is finally joining the fray. Due to their continued focus on cheapies and lack of depth and distribution at the crucial £7.99+ level, South Africa has slipped a lot. Chile has held firm, but Argentina is struggling to find its voice with competition from all corners of the globe putting pressure on its wines. California is starting to make waves again, which is good news. France has bounced back with the epic 2003 vintage and is performing well from all regions. Italy and Spain combined are up 5 to 39 – a stunning total for these hardworking nations. Germany is up to 9 wines, and this trend will definitely continue as more people discover the joys of Riesling. Portugal continues to hog the fortified wines, and Austria and England make up the numbers. This year really has been the hardest fought to date.

The **A-Z of Food and Wine** helps you find out which styles of wine go with virtually every ingredient in a food lover's well-stocked larder. You should also find most dishes from your favourite restaurant menu. I have been a restaurant wine consultant for over fifteen years and the *Daily Mail*'s wine writer for six. During this time I have worked with practically every famous chef in the UK, and there are very few dishes I haven't tasted, thought carefully about and then found a great bottle for. This section is crucial when you are eating out or entertaining at home.

The **Gazetteer** is *the* comprehensive list of the finest wineries in the world – it is the ultimate vinous who's who. It can be used when you are shopping for fine wine, when you are on holiday to track down the best estates to visit or drink from, or when you are in a restaurant with an unfamiliar wine list. It is completely re-written every year so it is also totally up to date.

The **Directory** is an essential compendium of the top independent wine merchants in the UK, plus their hometown or postcode, telephone number and, if they have one, email address. I have also included the HQ hot lines for the major supermarket and specialist wine retail chains.

AUTHOR'S NOTE

This year's Top 250 has been extremely difficult to put together. Not because I don't know where to find 250 awesome wines, but because I find myself going to the same brilliant sources year in, year out for this selection. The lack of new, cutting edge, innovative trade buying in the UK is getting me down. There should be more and more new wines in the UK every year, but we are somehow not seeing them in the numbers that we should. Most of the radical, boundary-pushing wines listed here, I found myself on my travels. Telling a winemaker that their wine is good and that I'd love to write it up is the impetus that many of them need. They then put pressure on their agents in the UK and force their wines to be shipped over here. This is good news – we get to drink new, fascinating wine and keep our thirst and wine diet satiated. But, while I enjoy discovering new wines and love to help the winemakers, it is not strictly speaking my job. Why isn't it being done by the legions of powerful, national wine buyers? This is my major gripe for 2005/2006.

Most supermarket and chain store ranges are getting smaller and the pressure on buyers is extreme, not only to make a profit but also to move stock. The UK has also lost two great, world-class buyers in the last year (poachers turned gamekeepers – they are now selling wine). Where are we to find the new talents? A buyer's job is to have a great (world-class) palate and, through their inspirational selection of awesome wines, inspire their staff and customers into pushing the boundaries of their wine knowledge. It is sad that their main job trait these days is simply to reorder the same old boring brands, week in week out, while forcing prices down to increase their margins. This endemic laziness is frankly demeaning to the millions of customers who rely on the buyers to help them drink better wine and (surely it's not too much to ask) excite them about this phenomenal subject. Readers of **THE WINE LIST** should boycott the crap wine on the shelves (remember I taste over 25,000 wines a year and only 1 per cent of them makes this book, so there is a lot of utter rubbish out there) and try to force the buyers into working harder to find better wines. We, as consumers, should also talk to our friends more about the great wines we have drunk and spread the word.

Despite my professional role as a wine writer and buyer, I had to battle even to get information about what wines are being stocked this year. I compiled the Top 250 with only two of the major stores' up-to-date wine lists. Some have not even been able to give me a wine list for six months. Without a wine list or their cooperation to find out what they have got in their warehouses, let alone what is due to come in, I have been forced to go it alone. For this reason there are more wines from independent wine merchants than ever before. There are also fewer sub-five pound wines. But, that is not a problem – this list sets out to tell you how to spend your money (wisely), not save it! A large number of estates and their wines pop up with encouraging regularity in the Top 250. These wineries and their winemakers are clearly the most consistent over-performers in the world of wine today and are to be applauded.

One day, I hope the wine world will again be run by wine lovers and not number crunchers. But until that dream comes true, rather than be perpetually disappointed, let's search out others who rejoice in great wines and drink them together!

THE TOP 250

£7.95 **Prosecco di Valdobbiadene, Endrizzi, NV**, Veneto, Italy (**Great Western**). There is no point trying to drop below the £8 with sparkling wines from Champagne or the New World. It is necessary to look to Europe and some of the classic styles of fizz to find solace. I have yet to be enamoured by a Cava at this mark, so one of the most famous, but least drunk (at least in the UK) Italian fizzies must do the job – Prosecco. I met Paolo Endrizzi years ago and he neglected to show me this wine, which is a shame because it is a dream and I might never have looked back. I am delighted to find it now, though – this is a very classy wine indeed. Those of you who follow the Top 250 every year will no doubt be intimate with NV Prosecco La Marca (£5.99, **Wai**), as it always had a slot. It is as good as ever but this year, and for only two pounds more, I cannot do anything other than say trade up and drink Endrizzi's Prosecco. *Salute!*

£7.99 **Jacob's Creek Sparkling Rosé, NV**, Australia (**Asd**, **Sai**, **Tes**, **Thr** and **Wai**). Last year, JC launched a cracking, dry, Shiraz rosé on us and it made my Top 250. This year, this massive but exceptionally well-run operation has gone one better with a triumphant and delightful cherry-red sparkling rosé. It is the definition of a crowd-pleaser, brimming with fresh, thirst-quenching, dry, raspberry and cranberry fruit, and an eminently affordable price tag.

£7.99 **Wolf Blass Red Label Sparkling Chardonnay/Pinot Noir, NV**, Australia (**Asd** and **Sai**). With a creamy, balanced, smooth palate and firm, refreshing acidity, this is a very good wine for parties and *al fresco* drinking. New to me, I was very impressed with this wine and I had no trouble finding a place for it in this year's all-star list.

£8.95 **Domaine des Baumard Carte Turquoise, NV**, Crémant de Loire, France (**Jeroboams & Laytons**). Baumard is a star performer in the Loire, most famous for beautiful, haunting, semi-sweet Coteaux de Layons. I have long marvelled at these wines, so when I came across this jolly-looking fizz, I was all set to be impressed. I wasn't prepared, however, to be completely and utterly knocked sideways. Fresh as daisies and bursting with creamy, citrus vitality, this is a heavenly glass of wine, which overshadowed a host of Champagnes that I tasted later that day – yippee!

£10.99 **Deutz Marlborough Cuvée, NV**, South Island, New Zealand (**Odd** and **Wai**). This is a justifiably famous Kiwi sparkler and it carries some serious Pinot Noir (wild strawberry) characters and great balance throughout the length and breadth of its impressive flavour. Don't ask me how to pronounce it though, as the wine trade has always been split between the *Doitz* and the *Durtz* camp – take your pick!

£12.99 **Green Point ZD, 2001**, Victoria, Australia (**Wai**). Green Point is a legend in the world of Aussie fizz – it is part of the Louis Vuitton Moët Hennessy empire. Winemaker Tony Jordan is a fastidious sort, but occasionally he shows a maverick streak bordering on the unhinged! Not only has he gone for a 'Zero Dosage' brew (i.e. no sugar and, therefore, bone dry), he has also sealed this stunner in crown-cap (like a beer bottle). Both moves are an immense improvement on any of his previous wines, as ZD can't now be 'corked' (no cork, no chance!), and it is tight, lean and nervy, as opposed to juicy, fleshy and a tad overweight. In short, this is a Catherine Deneuve at a Minnie Driver price.

£12.99 **Tigress, Bay of Fires Sparkling, NV**, Tasmania, Australia (**Bottleneck** and **Eagle's**). Arras is arguably Australia's most serious sparkler, and Tigress is its feisty, purring, young offspring. At half the price of a so-called 'famous' bottle of Champagne, this is a real steal. Elegance on the nose, depth of ripe fruit and finesse on the palate, and a long, savoury finish make this one of the wines of the year. It is a pity there is such limited distribution for this wine, but congrats to those wise merchants who have stuck their hands up early!

£13.95 **Layton's Brut, NV**, Champagne, France (**Jeroboams & Laytons**). The only thing that has changed between last year's Top 250 listed wine and this year's is the label. It is imperceptibly smarter – that is all. The recipe that makes this the best-value Champs in the country is still the same. Party planners take note.

£14.99 **Jansz Premium Vintage Cuvée, 2000**, Tasmania, Australia (**OFW**, **Philglas**, **Arthur Rackham**, **Sommelier**, **Stone, Vine & Sun**, **Tanners**,

Thos Peatling, Veritas and Vin du Van). There is a lot of wine in this bottle, in terms of flavour intensity and sheer complexity. If you tasted it blind, I bet you'd say this was a tenner more than its price tag. I adore Jansz, both the non-vintage and the vintage wine, but I think that this 2000 is winemaker Natalie Fryar's most impactful creation to date. It is a joy to drink – what more could you possibly want in a wine?

£14.99 **Pelorus Sparkling, Cloudy Bay, 2000**, Marlborough, South Island, New Zealand (**Harvey Nichols**, **Maj** and **Selfridges**). Strangely, I have always preferred the cheaper non-vintage Pelorus (an ex-Top 250 alumnus) to the flash vintage wine. Until now. This 2000 is more streamlined than the rather full-bodied 1999 and, consequently, it is far more my scene. Not as exotic or portly, but still pungently Pinot-scented, this is a very polished wine, and it is now a worthy big brother to its smart NV sibling. The Cloudy Bay name has always carried a lot of kudos and 2000 Pelorus is finally a worthy fanfare to the rest of the portfolio.

£16.94 **Tesco Finest Vintage Champagne, 2000**, France (**Tes**). Three cheers (or as many as you want) for this sprightly, uplifting, inexpensive, vintage Champs. The Tesco team has a good range of Champagnes and this is the pick of the bunch.

£17.57 **Schramsberg Blanc de Blancs, 2000**, California (**The Vineyard Cellars**). USA sparklers rarely get much airplay in the UK, but there is no name bigger than these guys and, considering the fact that this is a vintage Blanc de Blancs, the price is very competitive indeed. There is wondrous depth of fruit here and a very lively mousse (fizz) and it looks a million dollars, too.

£17.95 **A. Margaine Brut, NV**, Champagne, France (**The Flying Corkscrew**). Margaine is a name I have followed for the last few years and every time I taste this wine a huge smile appears across my face. The Flying Corkscrew is its UK agent, hence the amazing price, and if you are after inexpensive Champs, this is one of the best around. Ripe, effervescent, celebratory and elegant, this wine has it all.

£18.95 **Pierre Vaudon Brut Rosé, NV**, Premier Cru, Champagne, France (**Haynes Hanson & Clark**). Another small Champagne producer, shipped in by a Premier League independent merchant, Vaudon is a wicked little estate. Based in Avize, one of the prime spots for cool, crisp Chardonnay, Vaudon embellishes his portfolio with this wonderful, palate-titillating rosé by sourcing red grapes (Pinot Noir) from the nearby village of Ambonnay. Style-wise, these red grapes seem only to have been waved past the bottle, as the colour is ever so gently blushed with a salmon-pink hue. This sleight of hand makes for not only a stunning colour, but also a desperately chic and beautifully balanced wine. Refreshing, elegant and cracking value for money.

£19.50 **J. Dumangin Fils, Extra Brut, NV**, Champagne, France (**Yapp Bros.**). It is the year for bone-dry styles of fizz! This is another totally refreshing wine, but it is a lightweight in comparison with some of the others in this section. It cleanses and invigorates the palate as opposed to wrestling it to the ground. Clean as a whistle and made from 25 per cent Chardonnay, 25 per cent Pinot Noir and 50 per cent Pinot Meunier, this is the perfect apéritif wine. The tangy acidity and oodles of verve will slice through all manner of tricky canapés, and would also be a classic match with oysters.

£21.50 **Larmandier-Bernier, Terre de Vertus, NV**, Premier Cru, Non-Dosé, Champagne, France (**Vine Trail**). Another dry wine, Non-Dosé is extremely elegant, with layers of gentle, palate-soothing flavours and a minute's long finish. A favourite of the wine trade set, this is a pretty, floral wine and its delightful crisp finish is really uplifting. Value-wise, this is head and shoulders above any of the big brands at the same price.

£21.80 **Georges Vesselle, Brut Grand Cru, 1998**, Champagne, France (**Jeroboams & Laytons**). Small producer, Grand Cru, vintage Champs, a sniff over £20 – doesn't happen often, does it? Particularly when the flavour is £30's worth of anyone's money. Don't forget about this wine.

£22.95 **Leasingham Classic Clare Sparkling Shiraz, 1995**, Clare Valley, South Australia (**Philglas** and **Noel Young**). This is my favourite sparkling red wine on UK shelves. The 1994 made the Top 250 two years ago and it has been in purgatory waiting for this 1995 to spring into action. Some things, however, are worth the wait. Classic Clare is jam-packed with bright, shiny, plum and blackberry fruit. The colour is astounding, the nose invigorating and the palate, with its liberal dusting of sweet spices and white pepper, is a joy. Nothing will put a smile on your face quite like a large glass of this wine. I recommend cooking up a caveman-sized full English brekkie and opening a bottle of this on your birthday. Your feet won't touch the floor all day.

£23.99 **Moët & Chandon, Nectar Impérial Sec, NV**, Champagne, France (**Sai**). This is one of my favourite wines from the famous Moët & Chandon Champagne house. Made from a backbone of Pinot Noir, but expressing more texture and richness than many NVs, this is almost erotic, it is so silky and alluring. If you are new to Champagne and find the acidity on many examples too searing, this is a much smoother style that I'm sure you will adore.

£31.99 **Taittinger Prélude, NV**, Grand Cru, Champagne, France (**Luvians**, **Maj**, **Vicki's** and **Wimbledon**). The packaging may be a little dodgy – dark blue with gold bubbles – but the wine in the bottle is pretty serious. Made from a 50/50 of Chardonnay from Avize and Le Mesnil, and Pinot Noir from Ambonnay and Bouzy, this is a fleshier style of Champagne. By contrast to the other bone-dry wines in this section, this is a sexy, sultry, smooth wine, with more than a little curvaceous fruit and low-riding, Monroe-esque chassis. When you need a little romance, this Champagne might just be the prelude to a wonderful fugue. Watch out for deals – particularly from Majestic!

£32.00 **Bollinger, Special Cuvée, NV**, Champagne, France (**Berry Bros.**, **Fortnum & Mason**, **Maj**, **Odd**, **Sai** and **Wai**). There is something about Bollinger which challenges the drinker. The flavour is always richer than you remember it and the structure is firmer and more masterful. This flavour of vanilla and wild strawberries is heroic and the texture, uniquely Bolly's, is like getting up from a bed of Frette linen only to be embraced by a Hermès bath towel and then later enjoy a romantic walk around a gallery on the arm of an Anne-Fontaine-wearing beauty. Bollinger can turn fantasy into reality.

£33.95 **Roger Brun, Cuvée Des Sires, 2000, Grand Cru**, Champagne, France (**Liberty** and **Noel Young**). Based in Aÿ, the finest Pinot Noir producing village in Champagne (Bolly's HQ is there – no surprise), this super-cuvée from Roger Brun is utterly phenomenal. Made from 100 per cent Grand Cru Pinot Noir and described as 'ultra brut' (bone-dry in English), this wondrous elixir has considerable weight and depth, and all of this lustiness is, perhaps surprisingly, in perfect balance. A big mouthful of fizz, this could conceivably be drunk with main course dishes it is so persistent and intensely flavoured. A new find for me, Roger Brun has shot straight into my hot list of Champagnes.

£35.99 **Billecart-Salmon Blanc de Blancs, NV, Grand Cru**, Champagne, France (**Adnams**, **Berry**

Bros., **Fortnum & Mason**, **Odd**, **Uncorked** and **Noel Young**). Billecart have done it again with this splendid Blanc de Blancs (100 per cent Chardonnay). With a creamy, smooth texture, long, lingering palate and blessed with the most amazing, haunting, wild flower aroma, this is a very classy number indeed. It brims with breeding and distinction, like all of Billecart's wines, and, while it is not cheap, this wine can hold its own against other préstige cuvée Blanc de Blancs at well over £50!

£35.99 **Billecart-Salmon Rosé, NV**, Champagne, France (**Berry Bros.**, **Harvey Nichols**, **Lay & Wheeler**, **Lea & Sandeman**, **James Nicholson**, **Odd**, **Philglas**, **Selfridges** and **Noel Young**). There are very few apéritif wines that get my pulse racing as much as a glass of Billy Rosé. My mood lifts in a nanosecond and all of the stresses and strains of everyday life melt away. In fact, for the life of the glass (better still a bottle), I feel totally and utterly invincible. Imagine drinking wine that turns you into Han Solo or Lara Croft or whoever! There is no law against dreaming and Billecart Rosé is one of the dreamiest, most seductive wines in the world.

£36.00 **Ruinart, Blanc de Blancs, NV**, Champagne, France (**Amps**, **Bedales**, **Rodney Densem**, **Eton**, **General Wine**, **Handford**, **Harrods**, **Jeroboams & Laytons**, **Lea & Sandeman**, **Luvians**, **S.H. Jones**, **Roberson**, **Playford**, **Arthur Rackham**, **Vintage House** and **Wine Library**). This is one of the most attractive-looking bottles in the world. It is also, thankfully, truly scrumptious! Ruinart usually keeps its head below the parapet, but this year it has scored two wines in the Top 250, and they thoroughly deserve these listings.

£48.00 **R de Ruinart, Vintage, 1998**, Champagne, France (**Amps**, **Lea & Sandeman** and **Philglas**). This terrific new vintage for Ruinart is now on wine shop shelves up and down the country. It is heavenly, with broad brushstrokes of flamboyant fruit and exotic patisserie notes. I look forward to following this wine closely as it evolves – it should be a white-knuckle ride. Expensive and flashy, this is an unapologetically luxurious number but then, that's the whole point of serious Champagne, isn't it!?

£80.00 **Dom Pérignon, 1998**, Champagne, France (**Selfridges**). Scoop – I tasted one of the very first preview bottles of DP '98 back in June, with only two days to go before my deadline for this book! The pressure was on but I didn't have to worry – the first sniff and sip of this delightful wine sent my spirits soaring and, on pouring a larger glass to nose and cradle, I discovered one of the friendliest young DPs I have seen in ages. While I don't doubt this wine will age perfectly for twenty years, it is disarmingly delicious right now. Whether this is by design or not, I don't really care, because I would imagine that most people who buy or are given this famous fizz will uncork it and hope that the flavours live up to the hype. They would be disappointed if the wine tasted two decades too young but it's OK. Go for it – this wine lover says that you can drink '98 DP now! It is the most forward vintage for years and it is stunning.

£3.99 **Dolphin Bay Sauvignon Blanc, 2005**, Western Cape, South Africa (**M&S**). This is an aromatically accurate, budget Sauvignon Blanc from SA and it really grabs the attention. Citrus purity and racy acidity are the main themes, but there is grassiness and fresh herb outbreaks along the way. Cheers.

£3.99 **Pujalet, 2004, Vin de Pays du Gers**, France (**Wai**). Floral, lively and summery, this is a happy-go-lucky wine with a jaunty air and a cheeky little skip in its step. Delish.

£3.99 **Rapido Bianco Trebbiano d'Abruzzo, 2004**, Italy (**Boo**). Oof! It's hard to find quality wine below the dreaded £4 mark, but this cheeky little lass does the job well. With only about 35 pence worth of wine, at cost, in the bottle, chances are four pounders are going to disappoint, but Rapido (roll your arse, sorry 'r's) is crisp, dry, zesty, refreshing and citrusy. It looks pretty trendy, too. If you are up for a little double trouble, then have a go at Bianco's brother, 2004 Rapido Rosso di Beneventano, Campania (£3.99, **Boo**) – it is smooth, medium-weight and red-cherry scented. They are also both screwcap sealed, thank God, so rogue, stinky corks can't spoil the party!

£4.79 **San Valentín, Miguel Torres, 2004**, Catalunya, Spain (**Mor**, **Quellyn Roberts** and **Roberts & Speight**). You will find Torres Esmeralda in the aromatic section (where it has divine right, every year, to a slot in the 250), but this year a smart entry-level Torres dry white has crept in under the radar. Made from Parellada, one of the most mind-numbingly boring grape varieties on the planet (responsible for the lack of lustre in Cava), this neat, tidy, prim wine is simply breathtaking. A little like the librarian who takes her goggles off and shakes out her bun, San Valentín is a lip-licking beauty. Perhaps this is no surprise, as Torres is the consummate alchemist – the luscious tropical fruit and smooth, grapey finish is incredible.

£4.99 **Las Basca Uvas Blancas, 2004**, Castilla y León, Spain (**M&S**). Made by the brilliant winemaker Telmo Rodriguez, this fantastic wine is a blend of Verdejo and Viura (both pretty boring grapes without some serious alchemy), with a wicked fruity nose and a blindingly crisp finish. It is an unexpected joy and one of the best ways to dispose of a fiver – there is a lot of bang for your buck here. I guarantee raised eyebrows all round.

£4.99 **Muscadet Côtes de Grandlieu Sur Lie, 2004**, Fief Guérin, Loire, France (**Wai**). Look no further than this feisty number for sensational seafood matching. It's only a fiver, too!

£4.99 **Verdicchio dei Castelli di Jesi, Moncaro, 2004**, Marche, Italy (**Wai**). This is very smart wine for its diminutive price tag. Smooth, ripe, pear and apple fruit – antipasti never tasted so good!

£5.77 **Domaine Bégude Chardonnay, 2004**, Vin de Pays d'Oc, France (**Goedhuis & Co.**). Sold by the case only, this is the definitive unoaked French Chardonnay of the year. Made at the historic Limoux estate Domaine Bégude, now owned by a delightful, young English couple, James and Catherine Kinglake, this is the inaugural vintage of their baby Chardonnay. Already gracing dining room tables up and down the country (Goedhuis's private client list is a who's who, so add your name to it), this is a wondrous wine, which typifies Chardonnay's often ignored grace and style. You would have to trade up to Chablis at a tenner, to compete with the delightful, crystal clear, refreshing, apple- and pear-scented fruit in this beauty. It is also sealed with a screwcap, so each and every bottle will be in tiptop condition.

£5.99 **Gobelsburger Grüner Veltliner, 2004**, Kamptal, Austria (**Wai**). Made by the awesome talent at Schloss Gobelsburg (one of the finest estates in Austria), this Grüner Veltliner, a wickedly exciting, nerve-janglingly dry grape variety, is a total and utter bargain. The explosive, vivacious, citrus, pear and mint-leaf flavours leap from the glass and dive up your hooter. This is a wonderful apéritif style of wine and a stunning substitute for Sauvignon Blanc, if you fancy varying your wine diet and shocking your senses. And if you are taken with this wine, these guys also make a delish Riesling (£7.49, **Wai**).

£5.99 **Lugana Villa Flora, 2004**, Zenato, Veneto, Italy (**Wai**). Villa Flora has made it two years in a row in the Top 250, and it was up against some stiff competition. It is also the cheapest of the wines that I lined up for this space! The smooth, pear-

and apple-scented fruit is just as good as ever and the finish is classy and restrained. Full marks.

£5.99 **Sileni Unoaked Chardonnay, 2004**, Hawke's Bay, North Island, New Zealand (**Thr** and **WRa**). OK, I have a confession to make – this bottle is priced at £8.99 on the shelf, and bloody good it is, too, at that price. But Thresher and Wine Rack have this preposterous '3 for 2' thingy with all of their wines, so I am quoting the lower price for your delectation! Sileni's unoaked Chardy is a beauty, with crunchy pear acidity and a lovely floral palate. Get in!

£5.99 **Stormhoek Sauvignon Blanc, 2005**, Western Cape, South Africa (**Asd**, **deFINE**, **Harrogate**, **Odd**, **Sai**, **Thr** and **Veritas**). Jump on board, take a ride, yeah! This is a wickedly refreshing wine, with more get up and go than many bottles twice the price. Lemon sherbet and crunchy, ice-cold grapefruit juice jostles for position on the palate, and the finish is a live wire – crackling with 10,000 volts. If you remember the entry for Stormy's PG last year, you will be pleased to hear that it is back and looking fitter and foxier than ever – 2005 Pinot Grigio (£5.99, **Asd**, **deFINE**, **Harrogate**, **Thr**, **Veritas** and **Wai**).

£5.99 **Tesco Finest Gavi, 2004**, Piedmont, Italy (**Tes**). There is something wistful and romantic about Gavi, although I am not exactly sure why. Perhaps I need Paul McKenna's skills to find out but, even so, when a chic, tailored, self-assured Gavi sashays down my vinous catwalk I look up from my notes and reach for my camera. Found in Milan's most fashionable bars, Gavi (made from the Cortese grape variety) doesn't usually show this degree of class and breeding below the £10 mark. So get your Guccis on and snap up some of this bone-dry, delightfully refreshing, pear-, hazelnut- and apple-scented wine.

£5.99 **Viña Errázuriz Estate Unoaked Chardonnay, 2004**, Casablanca Valley, Chile (**D. Byrne**, **Luvians**, **Thr** and **Vicki's**). Crisp, lean, tight and keen describes the mood in this wonderfully nervy, green-apple-skin- and juicy-pear-scented Chardonnay. Made to combat Chablis and other unoaked, lunchtime-slotting favourites, Errázuriz has played a blinder here, and, taking the price into consideration, this is a real bargain. It is a screwy (twist top), too, and I love it. Bravo!

£6.49 **Château Saint-Jean-des-Graves, 2004**, Graves, Bordeaux, France (**Wai**). Half Sauvignon and half Semillon, this beautiful lime-juice-scented white makes a welcome change to Loire or Marlborough Sauvignon Blancs. It's seriously good value, too.

£6.49 **Salomon Groovey, Grüner Veltliner, 2004**, Kremstal, Austria (**Odd**). Silly name, silly label, but this wine is stuffed with dynamic, explosive, prickly, vivacious Grüner fruit. These untamed citrus notes and the buttock-clenchingly acidic finish make for a roller-coaster ride.

£6.50 **Picpoul de Pinet, Domaine des Lauriers, 2004**, Coteaux de Languedoc, France (**Press Wine Services**, **The Goods Shed Farmers' Market**,

LIGHT, DRY AND UNOAKED

Canterbury, Kent, tel. 01795 539293). I came across this wine by chance while enjoying a quick lunch at the Goods Shed (Clive Barlow, Master of Wine, has a stall there). What a joyous wine it is. Lauriers has the classic freshness and tanginess of Picpoul, but more depth of flavour than I have come to expect from this grape variety. So, from out of nowhere I discovered my favourite version of this unusual grape! That's the beauty of wine – at any moment a stellar glass can find its way into your hand.

£6.99 **Chapel Down Bacchus, 2004**, England (**Boo**). Make sure you don't get your Chapels confused in this section, as this citrus and fresh-herb drenched white is one of England's best wines, not an Aussie beauty. Having said that, I opened it for a top Australian winemaker the other day and he was mightily impressed! If you are in the mood for Sancerre or any other Sauvignon Blanc, stop and think again. Vary your wine diet and save a few quid with this terrific homegrown white.

£6.99 **Chapel Hill Unwooded Chardonnay, 2005**, McLaren Vale, South Australia (**Tes**). I tasted this wine with winemaker Michael Fragos when it was fermenting back in March and it looked great back then. The finished article is tightly wound and very exciting indeed. Crystal clear, wild flower and mild honey notes overlay a clean, core of apple and pear fruit. Sealed with a screwcap – so no worries there – and perfect with all light- to medium-weight starters and lunchtime dishes, this is a totally failsafe, crowd-pleasing wine.

LIGHT, DRY AND UNOAKED

£6.99 **Pazo Serantellos Albariño, 2004**, Galicia, Spain (**Tes**). Albariño is my favourite Spanish white grape variety. It has an intriguing nose not unlike a youthful, light Viognier, a smooth, sleek palate similar to Clare Valley Riesling and a zesty, refreshing finish, a little like Loire Sauvignon Blanc. The best ones are ethereal, vivacious, thoughtful and complex all at the same time. This cheeky, inexpensive wine is just that – clean, open, balanced and refreshing on first glance, but if you look beneath the surface there is plenty of intrigue interwoven with the tropical fruit. A smart tapas menu would do anything to be partnered with this wine.

£6.99 **Pinot Grigio, La Prendina Estate, 2004**, Lombardy, Italy (**M&S**). With great depth of fresh pineapple fruit on the palate and zesty, prickly lift on the nose, this is a delicious little wine that shows just how Pinot Grigio should taste. It rarely gets this good at this price.

£7.95 **Jurançon Sec, Domaine Castera, 2004**, France (**Ameys**, **Execellars** and **Great Western**). The nose on this Jurançon is so racy and intriguing that I suspect you might spend the first few minutes just sniffing away, completely forgetting about the palate. Quince, crisp pear skin, honeysuckle, sweet spices and fresh apples crowd the nose, but when the palate comes into view, everything changes and becomes less exotic and coolly linear. This shift in mood stretches out the flavour and it welcomes in a whoosh of acidity on the aftertaste that is simply gripping.

LIGHT, DRY AND UNOAKED

£7.95 **Mâcon-Chardonnay, Domaine Paul et Mallory Talmard, 2004**, Burgundy, France (**Haynes, Hanson & Clark**). Talmard's elegantly honeyed Chardonnays are the perfect antidote to over-oaked wines, because they see no barrels whatsoever. Yummy, creamy, smooth pear and apple fruit glides over your palate. This is wine at its most laid back and lovely. It is also fantastic value – Chablis lovers take note!

£7.99 **Wither Hills Sauvignon Blanc, 2005**, Marlborough, South Island, New Zealand (**Arriba Kettle**, **Ballantynes**, **Boo**, **Charles Hennings**, **Coo**, **Decorum**, **Edward Sheldon**, **Great Northern**, **Great Western**, **Michael Jobling**, **Odd**, **Old Forge**, **Oxford**, **Roberts & Speight**, **Simon Charles**, **Sommelier**, **Villeneuve**, **Wai**, **Wicked** and **Wine Society**). Winemaker Brent Marris (assisted by dynamic duo Ben Glover and Nadine Cross) has done the impossible and pushed this wine even closer to perfection. The weird thing is that I thought the 2001 vintage, which was in TWL '02, was perfect, so how does perfect get better? Don't ask me. All I know is that every year Wither Hills shows us that more can be done to fine tune and improve the legendary Marlborough Sauvignon Blanc recipe. In effect, it is more than just a wine that Brent is making, but a statement about the state of Kiwi Sauv. This epistle is well timed, because there are more vines in the ground than ever before and, sadly, more mediocre wines being made in the land of the long white cloud, too. Marlborough, let alone New Zealand, is not now a guarantee of quality, so beware. This 2005, tasted as a tank sample back in

LIGHT, DRY AND UNOAKED

May, was electric. Those of you who know me well and follow my writing regularly will not have a second thought about diving head first into this wine. If you are new to this book, then, perhaps this is one of the wines that in just one glass shows perfectly what I do.

£8.00 **Pinot Blanc Paul Blanck, 2004**, Alsace, France (**Jeroboams & Laytons**). I once described the Pinot Blanc grape as having as much character as the cardboard packing in a case of wine. Whoops – this version from Blanck is a stunner. Sealed with a screwcap, and with more silky fruit and honeyed spice than most Chardonnays, this is a very sexy wine. Super-smooth and sensual on the palate, it is a star – drink with everything and anything.

£8.40 **Quincy, Cuvée Villalin, Domaine Jacques Rouzé, 2004**, Loire, France (**Haynes, Hanson & Clark**). Forget Sancerre this year – I have found the wine for you. Made in the neighbouring village Quincy (pronounced Can-see), by the top producer Rouzé, this 100 per cent Sauvignon Blanc is drop-dead gorgeous. The vitality of mineral, herb, nettle, asparagus, lime and gooseberry fruit is unnerving. Take the plunge, head off piste and tackle this stunning wine.

£8.50 **Pinot Grigio Ramato, Visintini, 2004**, Friuli, Italy (**Lea & Sandeman**). Real Pinot Grigio is ever so slightly pinky/grey in colour (hence the true meaning/name of the grape). This wine has got to be one of the most beautiful shades of Grigio I have ever seen. What a relief then that the flavour lived up to the expectation. Get ready, because you are guaranteed to fall head over heels for this wine. It is luscious and silky, with grapefruit, melon and pear fruit, and a prickle of lively acidity runs its icy finger down the back of your neck when you taste it. Never has such an alluring PG delivered in such style.

£8.95 **Gavi di Tassarolo, La Zerba, 2004**, Piedmont, Italy (**Jeroboams & Laytons**). Crisp, crunchy, lemony and trendy – Gavi is such a fashionable wine, but I love it. Unfortunately there are so many dilute versions out there it is unbelievable. La Zerba, though, is a thoroughbred, and it will turn you into a snorting stallion in a trice.

£8.99 **Jackson Estate Sauvignon Blanc, 2004**, Marlborough, South Island, New Zealand (**Boo, Christopher Piper, Maj, Odd, Oxford, Sai** and **Wai**). Jackson Estate is one of the founding fathers of modern Marlborough Sauvignon. It is no surprise, then, that this is a textbook glass of wine. The nervy, asparagus, lime and elderflower fruit is perfectly balanced and, like all responsible Kiwi whites, it is sealed with a screwcap. So let's twist again. PS if you see the 2003 Jackson Pinot Noir (£12ish), don't delay because it is a cracker, too.

£8.99 **Labyrinth Chenin Blanc, 2004**, Wellington, South Africa (**deFINE, Handford, Harrogate** and **Veritas**). I know nothing about this wine except that when I first tasted it my notes bang on about fresh limes and honey ad nauseam. I gave it a mighty score and wrote that it was better than a number of other

LIGHT, DRY AND UNOAKED

very well-regarded wines, but, as I haven't tasted it since, I will be joining the queue to find out more!

£8.99 **Sainsbury's Classic Selection Pouilly-Fumé, 2004**, Fouassier, Loire, France (**Sai**). Spot on, classically dimensioned Sauvignon Blanc, from a good producer at a competitive price. If you are looking for a Caesar salad wine, this is it.

£9.99 **Craggy Range Old Renwick Vineyard Sauvignon Blanc, 2004**, Marlborough, South Island, New Zealand (**Wai**). Craggy makes cracking single vineyard wines and each year I have my own private battle between their three Sauvignons, Te Muna (Martinborough), Avery (Marlborough) and Old Renwick. All three are terrific, but my chosen wine has phenomenal complexity and length. I suspect that it gets drunk the second it is released, but in reality it needs a year to mellow and unravel its full array of charms. The brilliant 2005 arrives in November and the great Larry Cherubino has assisted Steve Smith this year in its production, so I can't wait.

£9.99 **Jack & Knox, Green on Green Semillon, 2004**, Wellington, South Africa (**deFINE**, **Harrogate**, **Odd**, **Veritas** and **Wine Society**). This is the finest Green on Green Semillon (and it really is neon green in colour) I have ever seen. Extraordinarily pure and very 'green' and lime juicy on the palate, this is a very pungent wine that can be sent into battle with some of the most assertive dishes of all time. It ages very well, too. So take the plunge and immerse yourself in this verdant pasture.

crackles in the *glass*

£9.99 **Longview Blue Cow Chardonnay, 2004**, Adelaide Hills, South Australia (**Odd**). I never really thought about the fact that this fantastic Chardonnay was unoaked until I had to put it into a section in the Top 250. The unoakedness of Blue Cow is not a problem in my mind, because this wine is so complete. It doesn't need augmentation from barrels, it just needs to be captured, bottled and then set free into your glass. Enjoy Blue Cow, it is as natural and fresh as a wine can be. I have it on good authority (thanks Duncan) that the '05 is a stormer, too.

£9.99 **Shaw & Smith Sauvignon Blanc, 2004**, Adelaide Hills, South Australia (**Andrew Chapman, Bennetts, Boo, Flying Corkscrew, Harvey Nichols, Hedley Wright, Moriarty, Oz Wines, Peckham, Philglas, Sommelier, Taurus, Villeneuve** and **Wai**). The 2004 is the best SSSB for years, managing to combine attitude and elegance in the glass. The 2005 is even more impactful and it will be on the shelves in the autumn. Martin (Shaw) and Michael (Hill-Smith) have found their feet again and these wines are an essential part of any committed Aussie wine diet. From the vital screwcap to the very last sip, this is one of the definitive Adelaide Hills Sauvignons and it virtually crackles in the glass, such is the energy and vivacity in the wine. 'Everything green' is the tasting note, and 'you'll need more than one bottle' is my addendum.

£9.99 **TK Sauvignon Blanc, 2004**, Adelaide Hills, South Australia (**Four Walls, Harrods, Sommelier** and **Uncorked**). Tim Knappstein (TK, geddit?) has

LIGHT, DRY AND UNOAKED

effortlessly strolled into the Top 250 with this iconic, benchmark Sauvignon. Rapier-sharp, tangy, more elbows than a roller derby and yet wonderfully lime juicy with elderflower and fresh herb moments, this is a very classy wine that will unravel languidly over the next twelve months.

£9.99 **Tyrrell's Lost Block Semillon, 2004**, Hunter Valley, New South Wales, Australia (**Eagle's**, **Hailsham**, **Peake** and **Vin du Van**). Benchmark Hunter Valley Semillon is traditionally drunk at around ten years of age. I must admit that I don't really like this style of wine that old, preferring to capture the adolescent energy and quizzical temperament of this noble grape in its youth. There are only three or four estates in the Hunter who are responsible for this region's global street cred and Tyrrell's is one of them. So with this responsibility and technical ability, just how good is the brand new Lost Block 2004? The answer is that it is bloody brilliant – a waxy, honey and lime-blossom classic. It's a shame that the rest of the world simply doesn't know about it yet. When they do, it'll cause a riot! It is ironic that the Old Guard in the New World has, until now, prevented new wine lovers in the Old World from drinking what I hope, one day, everyone will regard as a (new) classic style of wine.

£10.49 **Palliser Estate Sauvignon Blanc, 2004**, Martinborough, North Island, New Zealand (**D. Byrne**, **Connolly's**, **Halifax**, **Harvey Nichols**, **Hoults**, **Philglas**, **Sommelier**, **WineTime** and **Noel**

Young). The astonishing liquid in this glass is Palliser Sauvignon Blanc. It is a pure, aromatically cleansing wine, with a mass of perfectly balanced citrus fruit and a long, cool finish. Palliser hits the mark every year and the 2004 is no exception – it is one of NZ's best.

£10.09 **Blind River Sauvignon Blanc, 2005**, Marlborough, South Island, New Zealand (**Odd**). I was fortunate enough to be the first wine writer in the world to taste 2005 Blind River back in June. An ex-Wine of the Week in my column in the *Daily Mail*, Blind River is always a terrific wine and the 2005 is even more profound than the electric 2004. This time, passion fruit and ripe pear notes are intricately imbedded in the brittle citrus exoskeleton. The ripeness and precision of the fruit is almost unnerving and there is serious balance here and laudable length on the finish. Impeccable is a word I have used in the past about Blind River – I see no reason to change this flawless descriptor.

£11.99 **Keith Tulloch Semillon, 2004**, Hunter Valley, New South Wales (**Haslemere**, **Vin du Van**, **Wine Society** and **Noel Young**). Drink this goose-pimple-inducing Semillon any time over the next three or four years and you will be in seventh heaven. Another screwcapped bottle, Keith's wine can be drunk as an apéritif, with the freshest seafood, any salad, a cornucopia of Asian fusion offerings and even with main course fish, veal, pork or chicken dishes. Mr Tulloch is, technically, one of the Hunter's finest winemakers. He is a quiet hero and one with a

LIGHT, DRY AND UNOAKED

growing following. One thing Is for sure, if you have the occasion to taste this whip-cracking wine, and I hope you do, you will crave it again.

£11.99 **TerraVin Sauvignon Blanc, 2004**, Marlborough, South Island, New Zealand (**Cooden**, **Haslemere** and **Noel Young**). Vine-growing ace Mike Eaton knows every square inch of land in his beloved Marlborough region, so when he decided to plant his own vineyards he knew exactly what he was doing. The high-tensile, sprightly fruit in TerraVin Sauv is imbued with boundless freshness and lovely tight acidity. This makes it one of the UK's newest and brightest star wines. Track it down and be first in the queue for this vinous scoop.

£11.99 **Villa Maria Clifford Bay Sauvignon Blanc, 2004**, Marlborough, South Island, New Zealand (**Odd**). This is my favourite of the family of Villa Maria Sauvignons. In fact, I gave it a very rare 19/20 in my tasting notes. Clifford Bay is a cooler, more chiselled wine than many of its peers and it is a joy to nose and sip (it's screwed, too). Stunning with spicy food, its flavour could cut through armoured plating it is so pure, driven and intense.

£12.49 **Iona Sauvignon Blanc, 2005**, Elgin, South Africa (**Direct Wines**, **Philglas**, **SWIG** and **Wimbledon**). Raise your glasses because Andrew Gunn, proprietor of Iona, has finally decided to do the right thing and seal his celestial wine with a screwcap. Iona is now complete. I have followed this wine for years and as each vintage comes and

LIGHT, DRY AND UNOAKED

goes, it inches towards the perfect score. Now that a cork can't flatten (or indeed ruin) the flavour, we can, for the first time, taste the true, awesome quality of his Sauvignon grapes. Shockingly pure, bracingly dry and aromatically electric, Iona 2005 is a lesson in sheer class. Andrew and Niels Verburg's single-minded, tunnel-visioned, one-mission winemaking completes its brief – to excite, amaze, impress, refresh and satiate the drinker. I can finally say, with conviction, that this is the finest SA Sauvignon I have ever tasted.

£13.99 **The Lane Gathering, 2002**, Adelaide Hills, South Australia (**Bacchanalia**, **D. Byrne** and **Sommelier**). Made from 83% Sauvignon and 17% Semillon, and with a touch of oak (but not enough to take it out of this section, taste-wise), this is Australia's most intellectual answer to the Loire's finest Sancerres and Pouilly-Fumés. With John driving the metaphorical bus and Marty running the vineyards with consummate skill, the Edwards family team is now making some of South Australia's most gripping wines. I have tasted everything in this estate's cellar and they have block-booked places in The Wine List for years to come, such is the depth and quality of the waves of wines on their way to our shores. Gathering is way ahead of its time – sensitivity, elegance, power, presence and memory – it's everything you'd want from a serious glass of wine. If you want to experience yet more wizardry from The Lane, then 2002 Beginning Chardonnay (£16.99, **Bacchanalia** and **Philglas**) is thoroughly captivating, too.

£5.49 **Torres Viña Esmeralda, 2004**, Penedès, Spain
(**Amps**, **Odd**, **Tes**, **Thr**, **Unw**, **Wai** and **Noel Young**).
Five years in a row! Esmeralda is officially a
legendary wine. The screwcap seals in the phenomenal
burst of juicy melon, grape and pineapple fruit, and
the palate is as lush and sun-kissed as it always has
been. You wait a second or two for the acidity to
ratchet up its dryness, then it comes in like an old
friend slapping you on the back. There is nothing
better in the wine world than a dead cert, and
Esmeralda is one of these rare finds. Every time I
open this wine, someone falls in love with it, and at
a recent Indian food-and-wine matching masterclass,
it was voted the best all-rounder!

£5.99 **The Naked Grape Riesling, 2004**, Pfalz,
Germany (**Andrew Chapman**, **Charles Steevenson** and
Wai). If this wine can't get you guys excited about
German Riesling nothing will. Not only does it look
dead cool, it is also dead cheap and the flavours are
absolutely spot on. There's more – the Naked Ape is
sealed with a screwcap and made by Erni Loosen
(one of Germany's most charismatic and talented
winemakers). The flavours are bright, apply, grapey
and this is possibly one of the most refreshing white
wines I can think of. Imagine a vinous equivalent of
an ice-cold lemonade – spine tingling isn't it?

£6.30 **Les Grès Viognier, 2004**, Coteaux du
Languedoc, France (**Jeroboams & Laytons**). From
the same stable as the epic rosé, this is a textbook
Viognier, with blushing peaches and coy apricots
inhabiting the nose, and lusty lemons and buxom

buxom melons

melons sauntering around the palate. It is a good job the acidity comes in to save everything from getting too debauched. Brilliant winemaking and fab fruit = great wine.

£6.99 **Alsace Gewürztraminer, 2004**, Cave de Turckheim, Alsace, France (**M&S**). With a beautifully accurate lychee and rose petal nose, and succulent, fleshy palate, this is benchmark Gewürz. I see no reason to spend any more money than this on this variety, because Cave de Turck does the job so well. Waitrose has a very similar offering from the same winemaker at the same price, if you don't have an M&S near you.

£6.99 **Leasingham Bin 7 Riesling, 2004**, Clare Valley, South Australia (**Boo**). Staggering complexity, phenomenal grace and awesome value mark Bin 7 as one of the most enchanting Rieslings on the shelves today. The purity of the lime-juice fruit is unnerving and, once you've tasted this wine, you'll never want to let it go. 2004 Leasingham Magnus Riesling (£7.99, **Sai** and **Wai**), the baby sister to this phenomenal creation, is another beauty worth tracking down. I have been lucky enough to taste all of the 2005s from this historic estate and they are as invigorating and addictive as the 2004s. Life is better with these wines in your glass.

£6.99 **Mineralstein Riesling, 2004**, Rhine/Mosel, Germany (**M&S**). A quid better in flavour than last year, in my opinion, so before we've even started you've made £1! Does that make sense? Anyway, the

AROMATIC

delicious, cool, floral, grape, lemon, apple and melon fruit slips out of the glass and into your life with accomplished ease. This is Riesling at its most fluid and glistening – the perfect brain-chilling apéritif.

£6.99 **Villa Maria Private Bin Pinot Gris, 2004**, New Zealand (**Boo**, **Luvians**, **Vicki's**, **Wai** and **Wimbledon**). The best PBPG ever! Dryer and more age-worthy than most inexpensive PGs, this is a fantastic wine, brimming with true class and it rewards the drinker with a flavour that belies its affordable price tag. Hoorah – Villa is the most awarded winery in New Zealand, and this wine shows us why.

£7.50 **Dragonstone Riesling, 2004**, Rüdesheimer Drachenstein, Josef Leitz, Rheingau, Germany (**Odd** and **Weavers**). With a Tolkein-esque label and a marvellously evocative name – the literal translation of the vineyard itself in German – before you even open this wine you're excited. At only 8.5 per cent alcohol, and with a marvellous lick of residual sugar (a ripe juiciness on the aftertaste), this is the perfect lunchtime wine for sipping and chatting over on a lazy afternoon. Chill it down ice cold and you have yourself a very sexy apéritif to kick off some deep and meaningful conversations. If the Dragon gets you hooked, then graduate to the extraordinary 2004 Rüdesheimer Magdalenenkreuz Riesling Spätlese, Leitz (£9.99, **Boo**, **Hendersons**, **Lea & Sandeman**, **Luvians**, **Odd** and **Theatre of Wine**). This is a phenomenal glass of wine that soars and swoops on the palate like a…dragon, I suppose.

£7.75 **RK Estate Riesling, 2004**, Reichsgraf von Kesselstatt, Mosel-Saar-Ruwer, Germany (**Jeroboams & Laytons**). Annegret Reh-Gartner is the unstoppable dynamo behind this superb estate. She was kind enough to send over some sneak previews of her gripping 2004s and RK is a must for fans of spine-tingling Mosel Riesling. This terrific wine embodies the new style of Riesling in Germany. Fit, athletic, edgy fruit, with exotic, tropical moments, and keen, refreshing acidity – one foot in the past, on account of the length and class on show, but drier and more modern on the finish. The future is bright, the future is Riesling. If you fancy seeing what happens to these gorgeous wines as they age, 2002 Kaesler Nies'chen Riesling Kabinett (£10.35, **J&L**) is a true beauty, too.

£7.99 **Brampton Viognier, 2004**, Stellenbosch, South Africa (**Wai**). Brampton is the second label of the highly respected South African estate Rustenberg. This is one of the Cape's finest Viogniers, it is sealed in a screwcap and the flavours are absolutely accurate. Peach, nectarine, apricot kernel and lime blossom, it is all here! Brampton Viagra is performing miracles up and down the country.

£7.99 **Knappstein Three, 2004**, Clare Valley, South Australia (**Bibendum** and **Odd**). Winemaker (as opposed to fashion icon) Paul Smith has come up with this fascinating Gewurztraminer/Riesling/Pinot Gris blend, which is set to blaze a remarkable trail. It has taken ages for the Aussies to start to experiment with aromatic blends – the Italians are decades ahead – and if this debut is anything to go by, the rest

AROMATIC

should be joining the club soon! Three is a joy, with layers of exotic fruit on the nose and a fine, dry finish. Not one of the grapes dominates proceedings, preferring to use team-work to fashion a seamless flavour that effortlessly hypnotises the palate.

£8.99 **Albariño, Pazo Señorans, 2004**, Rias Baixas, Galicia, Spain (**Boo**). Booths continues to list some of the most individual and exciting wines in the UK. This is a model Albariño, and it is one of my favourite white wines on the planet. With a flavour that counter-points exotic fruit on the nose and fresh peachiness on the palate, with an eye-wateringly dry finish, you simply can't fail to come under this unique wine's spell. This is one hell of a ride for £8.99.

£8.99 **d'Arenberg Money Spider Roussanne, 2004**, McLaren Vale, South Australia (**Bibendum, Odd** and **Peckhams**). It is a joy to taste this remarkably self-assured, balletic Roussanne. While I don't doubt it will age well, it tastes amazing right now – brimming with white flowers, peach skin, greengage jelly and elderflower. Terrific with Asian-inspired seafood dishes, this wine has a lot of hidden power behind its wonderfully tailored Betty Jackson skirts. More black widow than money spider, I'd say.

AROMATIC

£8.99 **Graacher Himmelreich Riesling Kabinett, 2004**, Dr Loosen, Mosel-Saar-Ruwer, Germany (**Sai**). Only the top Sainsbury's stores stock this wine, so do check that your local branch carries it before sprinting down to the shops. When you pour this nectar into your glass you will catch the haunting, grape and apple aroma, and feel driven to dive into the glass – so make it a big one! Kabinett is a dryer style of Riesling, 2004 is a classically dimensioned vintage and Erni Loosen is a legendary producer. Add all of these elements together and this is a truly special wine at a fantastic price.

£8.99 **Ona, Riesling Viognier Chardonnay, 2003**, Rapel Valley Chile (**Odd**). A new name to me but one that I won't be forgetting, because this wine and its monstrous red friend, 2004 Ona Syrah (£8.99, **Odd**), are two of the smartest and most professional wines I have seen out of Chile this year. This white is a brilliantly balanced blend of three very characterful grapes and the lime, peach and honey notes are in perfect synergy. Blaze a trail today and own an Ona.

£8.99 **Pewsey Vale Riesling, 2004**, Eden Valley, South Australia (**Flagship**, **Odd** and **Sommelier**). Pewsey Vale's fabulous, dry Riesling is wonderfully aromatic and effervescent. It sports an uplifting, spritzy, pineapple and lime-zest theme, and the glorious finish is minutes long. While not overly tropical, that will develop over time, this is one of the yummiest apéritif or Asian-food-matching whites around.

£9.06 **Huia Gewurztraminer, 2004**, Marlborough, South Island, New Zealand (**Bibendum Wine**). I adore 'who-a-ya' and their stunning, aromatic wines. The beautiful thing about this Gewurz is, curiously, what it doesn't have going on as much as

AROMATIC

what it does. In the wrong hands, Gewurz can be a plodding, oily, sickly variety and, not surprisingly, Huia have no time for this unattractive style of wine. The restraint, finesse and haunting aromas of rose water and lychee make this an olfactory treat. On the palate the wine is slippery and slim-line, and it skates over the palate sprinkling sherbet and fruit-cocktail notes asunder. All in all this is a gorgeous wine and one that is perfection with spicy food.

£9.99 **Erdener Treppchen Riesling Kabinett, 2004**, Ernst Loosen, Mosel-Saar-Ruwer, Germany (**M&S**). I gave this wine a 19/20 in my notes after one short sniff and slurp. It is stunning, with beautiful style, elegance and momentum. Sealed with a screwcap and seemingly desperate for you to twist its top off, this is one of the most perfect aperitifs ever made. Crystal clear and lusciously fruity on the nose, but clean as a whistle on the finish. Erni makes heavenly wines, so here is a run down of a couple of other gems in the UK – starting with the awesome, crisp, groundbreaking and very widely available 2004 Dr L Riesling (£6.49, **Adnams, Ameys, D. Byrne, Cooden, Great Western, Peter Green, Harrogate, S.H. Jones, Luvians, Moriarty, James Nicholson, Odd, Oxford, Christopher Piper, Playford, Robersons, Sai, Edward Sheldon, Charles Steevenson, Unw** and **Wright**), and moving on to the desperately chic wine 2004 Bernkasteler Lay Riesling Kabinett (£10.39, **D. Byrne, The Cellar Door, Great Western, S.H. Jones, Odd, Philglas, Roberson** and **Charles Steevenson**).

AROMATIC

£9.99 **Tim Adams Pinot Gris, 2005**, Clare Valley, South Australia (**Australian Wine Club**). Tim's Riesling has made the Top 250 every year since its inception and this year's release, the 2005 Tim Adams Riesling (£7.99, **Tes**), is a very worthy wine indeed. In fact, it made the cut only to be relegated in order to mention this Pinot Gris. This is because, at the last moment, Tim promised to send the UK ten times the stock of his awesome, rare PG than we saw last year, so I had to tell you about it. This is a stunningly textured, melon, guava and pineapple-scented wine. At a tenner it makes Italian super-PGs look pedestrian. You must try it, because TAPG is only in its second year and you want to be a part of history in the making.

£9.99 **TK Riesling, 2004**, Clare Valley/Adelaide Hills, South Australia (**Handford** and **Wine Library**). This clever 75% Clare Valley/25% Adelaide Hills Riesling is one of the most complete wines I have tasted this year. Tim Knappstein knows both areas like the back of his hand but the idea of combining them as astutely as he has done is a new one to me. The purity and length of lime-juice fruit is astounding, in fact, it is frighteningly good for such a new concept.

£9.99 **Vis-à-Vis Viognier/Chardonnay by Linda Domas, 2005**, Fleurieu Peninsula, South Australia (**Bedales** and **Novum**). Once again, I have a scoop for you! I was the first person besides Linda and her team to taste this wine, and I can report that it is every bit as good (and perhaps even finer) than the 2004 that made the list last year. It is due to arrive in

AROMATIC

the UK in the autumn, so hoover up the 2004 asap, and then glide into this lusciously proportioned thoroughbred. The exotic Viognier fruit is tempered by the Chardonnay and, equally, the Chardonnay plumps up the fragrant Viognier. It is teamwork at its most synergistic. Linda is fast becoming one of the most inspirational, boundary-pushing, convention-disregarding winemakers in Australia. The wild pineapple, freesia, iced mango and lime zest notes in this wine made my neck muscles stiffen, like a cheetah catching the scent of its prey (luckily I didn't have to race off to catch this wine as the bottle was already in my hand). Total and utter luxury.

£9.99 **Yalumba Eden Valley Viognier, 2004,**
Eden Valley, South Australia (**OFW** and **Wai**). As the years go by this wine beds in more and more, and shows that Australia can rival the greats with the flamboyant Viognier variety. Winemaker Louisa Rose is widely recognised as one of the foremost proponents of Viog and for ten pounds this is one of the most complete on the planet. Everything is there – peach, apricot, lime, fresh flowers, nutmeg and so on…None of these elements are forced and the weight and lithe acidity make it a lot fresher than many other styles. If you want to drop three quid and taste Louisa's baby Viog, then 2004 Yalumba Y Series Viognier (£6.99, **Coo**, **Flagstone**, **Maj**, **Sai**, **Tes** and **Wai**) is a dead smart introduction to not only what she can do but what Australia is capable of with this luscious grape variety. Both screwcapped, both creamy and benchmark – Yalumba single-handedly powers this variety forwards.

£9.99 **Yering Station MVR, 2004**, Yarra Valley, Victoria, Australia (**Maj** and **Wai**). Yering's Marsanne/Viognier/Roussanne blend is back again, and this time it is finer, more honed, more lithe and racier. Once again the nose is a temptress, offering brief flashes of sensual promise. The palate slams the door shut with bracing acidity and fine corsetry. What will happen over the coming months is this wine will lose its inhibitions and you want to be there when its guard comes down! In my considerable experience of these things, the party will start with a flamboyant peach and lime nose, and follow through with a sleek curvature of rare proportions. That knicker elastic snapping acidity on the finish will give you a refreshing slap around the chops – but that always happens when you are having fun.

£10.99 **Pewsey Vale The Contours Riesling, 2000**, Eden Valley, South Australia (**Harrods**, **Hoults**, **OFW**, **Roberson** and **Vin du Van**). A change of variety this time for winemaking uber maiden Louisa Rose – now she turns her hand to Riesling. Pewsey's entry level wine is in the 250, a few pages back, but this is the big boy, and great value it is, too! Awesome fruit complexity underpins this historic wine, but make sure you give it some time in the glass, because it opens up like you wouldn't believe. Also, don't serve The Contours too cold, as this will kill the fruit. Patience is the watchword, and you will be rewarded.

£11.00 **Eitelsbacher Karthauserhofberg Riesling Kabinett, 2004**, Mosel-Saar-Ruwer, Germany (**Montrachet**). If you are really into Riesling and

AROMATIC

want to realign your taste buds like never before, try this wine. I visited the property this year and had a life-changing tasting. Once you've tried it you will want to move on to the even sexier Spätlese (£14.00, **Montrachet**).

£11.99 **Matakana Estate Pinot Gris, 2004**, Matakana, North Island, New Zealand (**Bacchanalia**, **Berkmann**, **Harvey Nichols**, **N.D. John**, **Luvians**, **Veritas** and **Wine Barrels**). The 2004 is the best ever vintage of this wine. It leaps out of the glass and, while it is not as fat as last year's curvy 2003, it wears a little more padding than the excellent 2002. The three or four months spent in oak barrels has lifted the nose and smoothed out the palate, and I can't recommend it enough to you. A perfect antidote to the Chardonnay blues, Matakana PG is a desperately talented main course fish and chicken wine with more than enough presence to tackle trickier ingredients, like saffron, curry and chilli heat.

£12.60 **Felton Road Dry Riesling, 2004**, Central Otago, South Island, New Zealand (**Jeroboams & Laytons** and **Sommelier**). As well as being the producers of some of the most incredible Pinot Noirs and Chardonnays on the planet, Felton Road also fashions awe-inspiring Rieslings. This wine is monumental. Not a keeper like the Classic Clare below (which could run for twenty years easily), this wine is already hitting the high notes. The nose is wonderfully perfumed, with an exotic nature that belies its steely core. The palate is racy and quick-witted, and you are left with a feeling that a bunch

AROMATIC

of well-dressed sprites and pixies have had a tango on your tongue. There is only one rule with Felton Road wines – if you see it, buy it.

£16.99 **Leasingham Classic Clare Riesling, 2002**, Clare Valley, South Australia (**Philglas**). You'll have to wait until the shipment arrives in November to grab a bottle of Kerri Thompson's greatest vinous achievement to date. But, hey, we have been waiting forever for Classic Clare Riesling to reach our shores, so what is a few more weeks. The fact that this is the most perfect vintage ever of this stunning wine makes it all the more important that you put your name down early for some stock. '02 CC is one of the greatest young Rieslings I have ever tasted (anywhere in the world) and, in comparison to just about every other category of wine you can think of, the value for money afforded by Clare Riesling, and in particular this bottle, is phenomenal. Total and utter class in a glass – iridescent, exquisite and mesmerising.

● ●

£5.99 **Blossom Hill Reserve Chardonnay, 2003**, California (**Mor** and **Sai**). I tasted this wine blind in a line up of nearly two hundred disparate Californian wines and it made it down to the last twelve. When I discovered what it was I was delighted – I had always been snobby about Blossom Hill. I learned my lesson – ignore the label, taste the wine.

£6.99 **Robert Mondavi Woodbridge Chardonnay, 2003**, California (**Asd**, **Sai**, **Som**,

OAKED

Tes and **Wai**). There is no bigger name in the USA wine industry than Robert Mondavi and this newly released Chardonnay is quite stunning. With true Californian appeal, rich fruit and sensitive oak, this is a lot of wine for the money. And to prove that it is not a fluke, the 2003 Woodbridge Cabernet (£6.99, **Asd**) is also benchmark. You can spend an awful lot of money on Californian wine these days, and often end up being disappointed. These two bottles over-deliver and I Hazard County a guess that you'll be Daisy with enthusiasm when you Luke at the quality in the glass and have a Bo at the flavour.

£7.99 **De Bortoli Gulf Station Chardonnay, 2004**, Yarra Valley, Victoria, Australia (**Tes**). Finely tuned, intriguingly layered and sympathetically oaked, this is a delicious wine that deserves a wide audience. It is great news then that Tesco has snapped it up – and its big brother the 2004 De Bortoli Chardonnay (£12.99, **Tes**). As this wine shows, the days of over-oaked Aussie Chardonnay are long gone!

£8.99 **Penfold's Thomas Hyland Chardonnay, 2004**, South Australia (**Asd**, **Maj** and **Sai**). Further improving on an already amazing recipe, Hyland 2004 is one of Australia's most important Chardonnays. Baby Yattarna (see later) is a quarter of the price of its starry stable mate. Totally and utterly crazy, and worth making serious mileage to find – this wine is very grand indeed.

£9.95 **West Brook Blue Ridge Sauvignon Blanc, 2004**, Marlborough, South Island, New Zealand

(**Abbey** and **Great Western**). There is a 20% oak barrel element in this wine, which means that I have taken it out of the unoaked section and put it in here instead. Can you taste the oak? Not really, its job is to pad out the sternum and augment the musculature a tad on this zesty but classy wine. The result is a complete, long wine with more depth than many Sauvignons – good work guys.

£9.99 **Green Point Chardonnay, 2003**, Yarra Valley, Victoria, Australia (**Adnams**, **Amps** and **Vicki's**). Wine guru Tony Jordan has been finessing this wine for years. The Holy Grail has been the balance between fruit, oak, complexity and freshness. It is now absolutely spot on and, as usual with Tone, he has over delivered because the value afforded here is incredible. A Grand Vin for a petit vin price.

£9.99 **Willows Semillon, 2002**, Barossa Valley, South Australia (**WRa**). This is blood and guts Semillon and it wears its heart on its sleeve. There is no pussy-footing around here because this is an epic, lemon-balm and lanolin-soaked wine. It is made to drink with masterful dishes such as roast chicken and chips, or even aioli – because it can handle the garlic mayo with ease. If you are cooking up a big boy's banquet, don't forget about Willows.

£14.50 **Leeuwin Estate Prelude Chardonnay, 2003**, Margaret River, Western Australia (**Domaine Direct**). With Leeuwin's main label hovering around the £40 mark it is important to know that you can buy the second label (which in 2003 is very close to

OAKED

Art Series in flavour) for a third of the price. If you have ever wanted to sniff and slurp a slice of Aussie iconography then this is it. If this wine were French it would be a Premier Cru.

£14.99 **Provenance Chardonnay, 2003**, Geelong, Victoria, Australia (**Handford**, **Philglas** and **SWIG**). Brand new to the UK – I was the first to taste the range – this is a tiny production, very smart wine and, having had a go at the rest of the range that includes a Pinot Noir, Pinot Gris and Shiraz, Provenance is here to stay. Utterly elegant, with breeding and understanding beyond its years, this is a fine example of just how graceful and delicious cool climate Australian wines can be.

£15.49 **Hardys Eileen Hardy Chardonnay, 2002**, Australia (**Noel Young**). This is one of Australia's best-value white wines. In any other country, this flavour (Grand Cru if ever there was one) would score £30 or more a bottle. But Hardys know their audience and reward them with wines like this. With every facet of the outstanding Chardonnay grape on display, you must taste Eileen 2002 – this is not only an amazing vintage but it is also a wine that blew 100 tasters away at a masterclass I was chairing earlier this year. We virtually had to call the paramedics when I let the price slip out. Buy it – you know you want to.

£15.95 **Shaw & Smith M3 Chardonnay, 2003**, Adelaide Hills, South Australia (**Bennett's**, **Boo**, **Flying Corkscrew**, **Liberty**, **Moriarty**, **Philglas**, **Sommelier** and **Noel Young**). This is another Aussie

OAKED

Chardonnay that is tightening up year after year. With more sensitive barrel treatment, but still the trademark lush palate, this wine is fleshy, ripe, succulent and moreish – a real treat.

£16.99 **Ken Forrester FMC, 2003**, Stellenbosch, South Africa (**Wai**). Ken Forrester is no stranger to this book. Every year he picks up a slot or two and, when I taste through the competition to find a usurper, no one quite captures the depth and expression of fruit in their wines that he does. This is a delicious, creamy, honey-, lemon-balm- and walnut-scented Chenin, and it is one of the world's finest expressions of this grape variety. Look no further for the perfect dinner party accompaniment to roast goose, a posh veal dish or a serious piece of fish. This is a very grown-up wine and one that lingers on the palate for minutes after every sip.

£17.50 **Bourgogne Blanc, Cuvée Oligocène, Domaine Patrick Javillier, 2003**, Burgundy, France (**Berry Bros.**). The balance in 2003 Oli is phenomenal. The tightrope walk between oak and fruit, depth and freshness, and power and poise is exact. This Bourgogne Blanc, from one of Burgundy's foremost alchemists Patrick Javillier, is rich, there is no getting away from it, but it is in no way over the top. I was shocked when I tasted it out of the barrel a year ago and then again in June when it was bottled – I usually prefer Patrick's more laid-back *cuvée* 'Forgets', with its intrinsic control and elegance, but, in 2003, Oli is the heroic brew – and I can't recommend it enough.

OAKED

£21.95 **Meursault, Domaine Vincent Bouzereau, 2003**, Burgundy, France (**Haslemere**). Beautifully balanced, with juicy, rich, fleshy, honeyed fruit and wonderfully perky, cleansing acidity, this is a stunning wine from a very warm vintage. For this reason it is ready to be drunk now, so you should leapfrog over any 2001s and 2002s, and shove this chap straight on to the dining-room table. Harvested from over fifteen *lieu dits* (individually named vineyard plots) and skilfully blended to capture the essence of Meursault (one of the most famous Chardonnay-producing villages in the world), this wine perfectly demonstrates that blended 'village' wines are often stronger and safer in 2003 than the much more expensive Premier Crus. Take the plunge and dive into a drop-dead gorgeous wine.

£29.99 **Penfold's Yattarna Chardonnay, 2002**, Australia (**Berry Bros.**, **Harrods**, **Odd**, **Selfridges** and **Wai**). The best Yattarna ever, sealed with a screwcap – a heady combination! The only downside is that there is very little stock, the price tends to shoot up when they get a write up, and margins vary wildly. So, I suppose all I can say is very best of luck! This is a seriously smart Chardonnay and one that stands shoulder to shoulder with the world's greats. It will age gracefully but I loved my first tasting back in March. My guesstimate for its peak is mid-2006 to 2010.

£100.00 **Ermitage Blanc, Ex Voto, E. Guigal, 2001**, Rhône Valley, France (**Waitrose Canary Wharf** and **Belgravia branches only**). Only made when the

OAKED

conditions are exactly right, this is one of the most awesome white wines I have ever had the pleasure of tasting – I didn't spit this one out! Only 8,000 bottles were made in 2001, from 50- to 90-year-old vines and Waitrose has grabbed a tiny parcel to sell from its two prestige wine stores. The colour, complexity and length of this wine are all astounding. Made from 95 per cent Marsanne and 5 per cent Roussanne the flavours orbit the olfactory system flinging out starbursts of white peach, wild honey, nectarine stones, lavender, ancient cognac, sweet wood smoke, Floris Cefiro body cream and aniseed. You could spend years dissecting this wine and, the good news is, you have them – I think EBEV will age gracefully for two decades!

●●●●●●●●●●●●●●●●●●●●●●●

£5.50 **Les Grès Rosé, 2004**, Coteaux du Languedoc, France (**Jeroboams & Laytons**). Les Grès is made from a traditional blend of Grenache and Syrah, and it is the lightest and freshest of this section's wines. The perfect apéritif and canapé wine, it is stuffed with ripe cherry and mulberry flavours, with a dusting of spice and a punchy, dry, refreshing finish.

£5.99 **Stormhoek Select Rosé, 2005**, Western Cape, South Africa (**Asd**, **deFINE**, **Maj**, **Thr** and **Veritas**). With a Shiraz/Pinotage frame that is refreshed with all manner of other bits and pieces Stormy Pants Rosé was the rock 'n' roll hit of TWL '05. The 2005, with much larger distribution, is even finer – capturing the vital redcurrant essence aroma, staggering élan on the palate and a healthy dose of S&M spanking acidity on the finish. If you missed out on tasting this wine last year, then shame on you! Make up for it this year and you'll see what all of the furore is about.

£5.99 **Torres San Medin Cabernet Sauvignon Rosé, 2004**, Curicó Valley, Chile (**Boo** and **Wai**). Cabernet Sauvignon is not usually associated with rosé wines, but Torres is always one to break with tradition, and this wine is a stunner. There are delightful blackcurrant, black cherry and elderberry notes on the palate, and, like every other wine in this section, it is bone dry. You could drink this wine with as disparate a selection of dishes as a lamb curry, lobster salad, tomato soup, sausages and mash, pan-fried red mullet or Diablo chilli pizza! Better still, chill it ice cold for the perfect apéritif. The 2005 appears in the late autumn and it is also a stunner.

£6.49 **Villa Wolf Pinot Noir Rosé, 2004**, Pfalz, Germany (**Bottleneck**, **Connolly's**, **Henderson**, **S.H. Jones**, **Sai**, **The Vineyard** and **Wimbledon**). Wine wizard Erni Loosen proves that 'anything you can do I can do better'. This beautiful, aromatic, raspberry-scented, feather-light rosé is not only a stunner to look at, it is also thrilling in the glass.

£6.95 **Otto Bestué Rosé, 2004**, Somontano, Spain (**Cheshire Smokehouse** and **Great Western**). This is an utterly amazing wild-cherry-scented rosé, with vibrant fruit and beautiful herbal elements. Despite being an ancient estate, the Bestué family is at the cutting edge of technology and modern winemaking. This rosé is joyous. In fact, I am smiling now, so strong is my memory of this wine.

£6.99 **Louis Jadot Rosé, 2004**, Burgundy, France (**D. Byrne**, **Luvians**, **Peckhams**, **Thr**, **Vicki's** and **Wimbledon**). Hailing from Mâcon and looking about as pretty a bottle of wine as I have ever seen, this is screwcap-sealed, stunning, palest pink and hauntingly beautiful. Light, fresh, ethereal and eminently gluggable, I suspect that it will fly off the shelves on looks alone and then wow people's palates when they pour a glass. Too light to really attack food with any huge success, I reckon this lovely wine is best served with canapés and light starters. Unlike Yorkie bars, this one's for the girls.

£7.49 **Matahiwi Estate Rosé, 2004**, Wairarapa, New Zealand (**Odd**). Made from Pinot Noir, this wine is a very surprising number indeed. The reason for my bewilderment is that Sancerre rosé, Pinot Noir's smartest rosé incarnation, always seems so underpowered (a fashion victim's folly), so how can this wine be so awesome? The trick is that the fruit from this terrific estate is seriously ripe and they have cleverly shoved a dollop of juicy Merlot in to help it out, too. This inspirational winemaking has resulted in a gob-smackingly serious glass of wine. The flavour – pick-your-own everything in a glass – is amazing, and I drank it with an Indian banquet the other day and it was incredible. If you want to taste the grown-up red version of this

wine, then 2004 Matahiwi Pinot Noir (£8.49, **Odd**)
is only £1 more, which makes it one of the best
value Pinots in this book.

£8.49 **Shotbull Shiraz Rosé by Linda Domas,
2005**, Fleurieu Peninsula, South Australia (**Bedales**
and **Novum**). This dramatic rosé is made from
sensational Shiraz grapes. It is brassy, big, bold and
beautiful, and the fruit flavours cover every red and
black berry imaginable. When matching to food, it
behaves more like a red than a rosé, as there is a
sturdy backbone here and masses of energy in the
glass. Another screwcap-sealed number, this is the
perfect picnic wine, too, as you can chill it right
down and then gradually allow it to warm,
whereupon it will change from drinking like a white,
to drinking like the Aussie Shiraz it really is! Linda
has shot to stardom in two vintages and every one
of the preview wines she sent me back in June was
spectacular. In theory she could have scored nine in
the 250 – but I had to exercise some restraint. I can
assure you I don't have this kind of control when I'm
enjoying these stellar wines at home!

£8.99 **Château de Sours Rosé, 2004**, Bordeaux,
France (**Corney & Barrow**, **Goedhuis & Co.**, **Maj**,
Playford and **Tanners**). The 2003 Sours Rosé (ex-Top
250) was always going to be a hard act to follow –
as it was such a juicy, rich, intense style of wine.
However, this slim, sleek, sexy 2004 is a very worthy
successor. This wine has a cult following in the UK,
so don't delay – grab some stock before it runs out.
The cool, calm Merlot grapes that form the red-

cherry core of this smart rosé are of the very highest calibre. Bottled with a screwcap for perfection, 2004 Sours Rosé is a must for chic lunch parties and it is another star player with fusion cuisine.

£8.99 **Turkey Flat Rosé, 2005**, Barossa Valley, South Australia (**Edencroft**, **Harrods**, **Nidderdale**, and **Noel Young**). Turkey Flat is an historic estate in the famous Barossa Valley and it is widely acknowledged as one of the New World's foremost rosé producers. Made from a bizarre and wholly original blend of Grenache, Cabernet Sauvignon, Shiraz and Dolcetto, this is one of the most ballistic 2005 rosés I have seen. With a beguiling cranberry and spicy-red-berry nose and a plush, medium-weight palate, this is a very erudite wine. Bone dry and well balanced, this is Australia's most complex rosé that can be drunk at every occasion imaginable.

• •

£2.66 **Vineyard X Garnacha, 2004**, Campo de Borja, Spain (**Thr** and **WRa**). Single bottle price £3.99, three for the price of two, £2.66. Make your mind up time, because this is a lovely, little, spicy, blackberry-imbued winter warmer.

£2.99 **Gran Tempranillo, 2004**, Cariñena, Spain (**Sai**). Assuming you have a coach-load of people coming along to a party in the next few months, you'll need a hearty, funky red that isn't going to let the side down or break the bank – this is it! And if you happen to be a party animal and have one every

FRUIT-DRIVEN

weekend, you can ring the changes with this wine's twin brother, 2004 Gran Garnacha (£2.99, **Sai**). Both boast ripe red fruit and lovely savoury finishes. What more could you want? Needless to say, I am not a fan of sub-four-pound wine as a rule so, when a sub-three-pound wine comes along that makes the grade, it is time to take note!

£3.05 **Cuvée de Richard Rouge, 2004**, Vin de Pays de l'Aude, France (**Maj**). Majestic virtually owns this slot with its awkwardly named house wine. I have used this red for parties in the past and everyone has been jolly happy with the flavour. The fruit is clean, juicy, smooth and light – it does exactly what it says on the tin. Clever Dick.

£3.49 **Les Marquières Rouge, 2004**, Vin de Pays de Coteaux de Fontcaude, France (**Maj**). Turn the volume on Richard up one notch and relax with the safety of a screwcap. Marquières is another budget pocket rocket.

£5.98 **Kiss Chasey, Cabernet/Shiraz/Merlot, 2004**, Western Australia (**Asd**). Quirky name, cheeky label, screwcap-sealed and really very, very good indeed. Top class fruit from WA very rarely comes in at this sort of price. This is a lush, juicy-berry style of red, forward drinking and, as far as food-and-wine matching is concerned, you can throw the rulebook out of the window (metaphorically, of course, don't throw this one!). It is an all-purpose crowd-pleaser that works perfectly from the time the gun goes off (midday, in my case) until close of play.

FRUIT-DRIVEN

£5.99 **Jacob's Creek Merlot, 2004**, South Eastern Australia (**Asd**, **Sai** and **Tes**). JC Merlot is a wondrous little wine. The flavour is pristine, with jammy, cranberry, red plum and cherry fruit. The palate is smooth and the finish is very tidy and refreshing. Three cheers JC! At £5.99 this wine is going to make a lot of people happy.

£5.99 **Marqués de la Concordia Signa Tempranillo, 2003**, Rioja, Spain (**Odd** and **Tes**). This is an utterly stunning, light-weight Rioja. Don't expect classic Riojan here – Benylin, raspberries and old oak nastiness (I can't stand old-style Rioja, in case you hadn't guessed!). Signa is a delicious, inexpensive, modern, expressive, red-fruit-driven Spanish red. It is much lighter and fresher than you might imagine and this makes it one of those rare reds that you could conceivably drink on its own. But, if you had a ploughman's, rogan josh, soss and mash, or any other comfort food on the go, it still manages to impress. 2003 is a phenomenal vintage and this wine shows why – awesome and unmissable, Concordia is a name to follow. I know because I have tasted the entire range and it is magnificent.

£6.55 **Château Puyanché, 2002, Côtes de Castillon**, Bordeaux, France (**Haynes, Hanson & Clark**). Cheap red Bordeaux is a vile category but this is a superb wine. For every hundred bottles I see I am likely to only find two or three that I like. To get into the Top 250 at this price point the wine has to be awesome, and Puyanché is. Enjoy this rare slice of quality from the biggest wine region in the world.

FRUIT-DRIVEN

£6.99 **Beaujolais-Villages, Combe aux Jacques, Louis Jadot, 2004**, Burgundy, France (**D. Byrne**, **Luvians**, **Peckhams**, **Tes**, **Vicki's**, **Wai** and **Wimbledon**). 2003 was a brilliant, if small, vintage in Beaujolais. 2004 shows what a difference a year makes. Finer, more sophisticated and yet packed with that classic summer pudding juice and crunchy acidity on the finish, this is another virtuoso performance from the pantheon of Jadot greats. Do make sure you give it fifteen minutes in the fridge, just to tighten and augment the fabulous fruit flavours, and you'll see the nose whoosh out of the glass in time-honoured fashion. I raise my glass of this wine, to this wine!

£6.99 **Secano Estate Pinot Noir, 2004**, Leyda Valley, Chile (**M&S**). Velvety plum fruit, with one of the silkiest finishes imaginable, this is a ridiculously yummy wine and, such is its charm, it would romance even the most reluctant red wine drinker.

£7.99 **Swan Bay Pinot Noir, 2004**, Scotchmans Hill, Geelong, Victoria, Australia (**Odd** and **Wine Society**). New Zealand, with its proud heritage of Pinot Noir production, might begin to feel very concerned if more sub-tenner, awesome-quality Pinots like this wine emerge from Australia. Andy Browne, son of David and Vivienne Browne, is now based in the UK, spreading the word about his wines directly to his most important world market – us. This shows just how serious Australia and Scotchmans is about you, the serious, committed, quality-conscious wine lover. 2004 Swan Bay is a wine that belongs in your cellar. Screwcapped, bright, pure, aromatic and heaving

meaty little bugger

with berry fruit, you will not believe just how gorgeous this wine is.

£8.49 **Tamar Ridge Devil's Corner Pinot Noir, 2004**, Tasmania, Australia (**Charterhouse, Compendium, Great Western, Novum, Oz Wines, Weavers, WineTime** and **Noel Young**). With more depth, weight and dark fruit than the Swan Bay above, this is a meaty little bugger and one that shows how far and fast Tasmania has come on in the Pinot competitive world. If I poured this wine out for a load of wine bores and asked them where it came from and how much it cost, the answers would be so wide of the mark it would be extraordinary. Tamar is set to be a very famous estate, particularly if this label can grow – at £8.49 you will be gob-smacked, spellbound and mesmerised.

£8.70 **Chiroubles, Domaine de la Grosse Pierre, Alain Passot, 2004**, Beaujolais, France (**Haynes, Hanson & Clark**). With a notch more intensity and a slightly weightier feel than the Jadot B-V, this Beaujolais Cru – from one of the recognised ten best villages, in this instance Chiroubles – is sublime. Passot is one of the most talented Beaujolais producers and there is a whisper of black fruit embedded in this heady red fruit cocktail. What amazes me is that, for one of the most renowned wine regions in the world, the top offerings can cost as little as £7.81 by the case!

£9.99 **Avila Pinot Noir, 2003**, San Luis Obispo, California (**Odd**). Top-quality Californian Pinot Noir,

FRUIT-DRIVEN

more often than not, costs a fortune but this wine has all the attributes of a wine twice its price, including a wild strawberry nose, velvety smooth palate and mesmerising finish. I feel confident that if you like red wine, you'll be amazed by this wondrous bottle. Avila has always been a star estate, but the 2003 vintage is a dreamboat. All you have to do is find someone to share it with.

● ●

£4.99 **De Bortoli DB Selection Cabernet/Merlot, 2004**, Riverina, Australia (**Odd**). De Bortoli is fast becoming a force to be reckoned with. Chardonnay, Shiraz and Pinot Noir feature in this list and, not content with this haul, an entry-level Cab/Merlot stumbled across my path and I couldn't leave it out of the reckoning. This wine is bloody brilliant! Juicy, mouth-watering, beautifully ripe and dead cheap.

£4.99 **Las Basca Uvas Tintos, 2004**, Castilla y León, Spain (**M&S**). This is the chunky little brother to the pretty little white in the unoaked chapter. Telmo has, once again, played a blinder. Made from Tempranillo, this is a wickedly impressive, black-fruit frenzy, with plum and coffee on the palate, and a fabulously velvety finish. I can't recommend this wine enough.

£5.33 **Cazal Viel, Grande Reserve Syrah, 2003**, St-Chinian, Languedoc, France (**Thr** and **WRa**). £7.99 is the single bottle price and £5.33 is the three for two price. I like this wine at £7.99, but I adore it at a fiver. The density and tar in this wine is very alluring, and the spice and power on the mid-palate also catches the St-Chinian mood perfectly.

£5.99 **Leasingham Magnus Shiraz/Cabernet Sauvignon, 2002**, Clare Valley, South Australia (**Thr**). Once again, I've listed this under its '3 for 2' price – it should be £8.99 on the shelf – either way it's a bargain! Shiraz/Cabernet is a classic, but seemingly long forgotten, blend in Australia. Leasingham makes one of the definitive versions and keen drinkers will adore this brilliant 2002. Wallow in the heavenly, spicy, mellow, enticing red- and black-fruit flavours while laughing at your teeny credit card receipt. With total synergy in the glass, a minute's long finish and another two bottles under the stairs, I bet you'll be feeling pretty happy.

£5.99 **Manta Preta, 2003**, Estremadura, Portugal (**Wai**). Red grapes Tinta Roriz and Touriga Nacional usually spend their time in port, but here they are put to fantastic use. The violet, blueberry, liquorice and vanilla flavours are amazing and fascinating at the same time. Be brave and try something new.

£5.99 **Marqués de Griñon, 2003**, Rioja, Spain (**Maj**, **Mor**, **Sai**, **Tes**, **Thr** and **Unw**). 2003 was a first-class vintage in Rioja and Griñon played a blinder. This is a terrific glass of wine that has one foot in the past and the other in the future. Respect for the region, its history and cutting-edge technology in seamless harmony. Why it is only £6 is a mystery.

£5.99 **St Hallett Gamekeeper's Reserve, 2004**,

MEDIUM-WEIGHT

Barossa Valley, South Australia (**Bacchanalia**, **Bibendum**, **Cellar Door Wines**, **Coo**, **Harvey Nichols**, **N.D. John**, **Maj**, **Odd**, **Sommelier** and **Wai**). If you're not already a convert to St Hallett wines, then get a bottle of Gamekeeper's because, even though it is their cheapest red bot, it is a star wine. Made from Shiraz, Grenache, Touriga (a port variety) and Mourvèdre (most famous in Provence), this is a totally inspirational blend that is as much at home at a barbie, as it is with a wintry stew. The only thing you need to tweak is the temperature. Chill for the summer and keep it cool, not cold, for the winter. This schizophrenic red, made by Matt Gant (a young Brian Blessed) is, on the one hand, a frenzied glugger and, on the other, a one-thousand-piece jigsaw. This is what makes it so brilliant, inspirational, zany and addictive. St Hallett is a great label to rely on and an oasis in the deserts of mediocre crap served up in some dodgy wine departments. If you want to see what Matt can do with no upper limit, then track down 2003 St Hallett Blackwell Shiraz (£12.99, **Bibendum**, **Oz Wines**, **Richards & Richards** and **Noel Young**). Drink this when you feel you are able to cope with a colossal onslaught of flavour.

£6.55 **Mas Collet, 2002**, Montsant, Celler de Capçanes, Tarragona, Spain (**Wai**). This Garnacha, Tempranillo, Cariñena and Cabernet Sauvignon blend is a dreamboat. It spends a brief spell in oak barrels and then zips over here for our delectation. The spiky cranberry, red cherry and mulberry fruit is astonishing. Get out your Spanish cookbooks and get busy in the kitchen – let this wine be your inspiration.

MEDIUM-WEIGHT

£6.99 **Capitel dei Nicalo Valpolicella Classico Superiore Appassimento Breve, 2003**, Tedeschi, Veneto, Italy (**Sai**). For pasta, pizza and all other Italian dishes look no further than this terrific Valpol. With masses of acidity, punchy plum and cherry fruit this is the wine to cut through cheesy and meaty sauces with style.

£6.99 **Cumulus Rolling Cabernet/Merlot, 2003**, Orange, New South Wales, Australia (**Wine Cellar**). Philip Shaw is a legendary winemaker and his intricate craftsmanship is on display in this inexpensive, yet grippingly impressive red blend. Cool climate Orange's future looks rosy with this sort of stylish Bordeaux-decimating wine flooding on to the market. If Rolling Cab/Mer gets you revved, then don't miss the brand new 2004 Cumulus Climbing Merlot (£8.99, **Maj**). With autumn and Christmas deals in Majestic bringing this phenomenal, dark plum and berry-soaked wine down to £6.49 and £6.99 respectively (if you buy two bottles), this is one of the most exciting and unmissable new wines on the shelves today.

£6.99 **Da Luca Alto, Barbera d'Asti, 2003**, Piedmont, Italy (**Som**). This is a naughty number, with masses of extract, pumped-up plums and black cherry fruit. The acidity is refreshing and crisp, and it will cut through massive dishes with consummate ease. Alto? You'll be a Soprano with a bottle of this under the bonnet.

£6.99 **Montes Limited Selection Cabernet/ Carmenère, 2004**, Colchagua Valley, Chile

MEDIUM-WEIGHT

(**Maj**). Spot on fruit – a heavenly combo of blackcurrant and raspberry – topped off with a liberal sprinkling of mocha. Montes always impresses and this entry level wine is one of the most complete in the range. Watch out for deals – Majestic always comes up with something interesting around Christmas.

£7.49 **Rosemount Estate Diamond Label Merlot, 2002**, Australia (**Tes** and **Unw**). The 2002 vintage was so cool and calm that aromatic red grapes like Merlot performed really well. Rosemount managed to capture the haunting red perfume and silky texture of this variety perfectly, and if you are a fan of smooth wines, then this Merlot, with no grip at all, will slip down a treat.

£7.50 **Preece Merlot, 2003**, Nagambie Lakes, Victoria, Australia (**Bibendum** and **Oz Wines**). With an unexpected extra dimension of red fruit that rebounds off the back palate, this is a surprising and downright delicious wine. Smooth, cultured and unruffled, it is a sofa-sipping delight.

£7.95 **Château La Hase, 2003**, Bordeaux, France (**Lea & Sandeman**). Smooth, drinking beautifully and with just the right amount of blackcurrant energy and Old World charm, this is a cracking bottle of red Bordeaux. Trust Charles and Patrick (**L&S**) to come up trumps. They would rather sell nothing than have a sub-standard wine on their shelves, and when I asked to see some wines the other day, the two red Bordeaux they showed me jumped straight into this list. Bravo!

MEDIUM-WEIGHT

£7.95 **Rey Don Garcia Rioja Crianza, 2002**, Bodegas Ruconia, Spain (**Lea & Sandeman**). This is yet another terrific wine from the never-ending source of excellence that is the Lea & Sandeman cellar. Tasting like a wine worth twice the price, this is unmistakably Rioja but so much better than many other samples that I have tried over the last twelve months. The purity of plum and mulberry fruit, with its whisper of vanilla bean and green leaf, is incredible.

£7.99 **Château Ségonzac, 2003**, Premières Côtes de Blaye, Bordeaux, France (**Wai**). The 2002 made the list last year but this 2003, from the warmest vintage on record, is even better. In fact, it is a ripper! Now sealed with a screwcap and pumped up with fruit, you should take a test drive with this wine.

£7.99 **Harrowgate Shiraz, 2003**, Central Victoria, Australia (**M&S**). Made by the dynamic duo Toby Barlow and Don Lewis at the excellent Mitchelton estate, this is a perfectly plummy, spicy, blackberry- and leather-scented winner. And it's cheap for the skill and raw materials involved, I can assure you. It's also too easy to drink – sorry!

£7.99 **Nepenthe Charleston Pinot Noir, 2003**, Adelaide Hills, South Australia (**WRa**). Another '3 for 2' (the one bottle price is £11.99), grab three bottles for £23.98 and you're laughing. Lush, mellow and densely flavoured, this is the Pinot of the year at £7.99.

£7.99 **Oyster Bay Merlot, 2004**, Hawke's Bay, North Island, New Zealand (**Maj**, **Sai**, **Unw**, **Wai** and

MEDIUM-WEIGHT

Wimbledon). I have been waiting for this wine to finally come up to speed and in 2004 it has really hit the mark. Screwcapped and bright as a button, this medium-weight, lunchtime-style Merlot is just the ticket for lighter meaty dishes and pizza and pasta frenzies. Red-fruit driven and with a delightful herbal twist on the finish, this is one of those wines that likes to be chilled a few degrees to really show off its aromatic nose and lithe chassis.

£7.99 **Seigneurs d'Aiguilhe, 2003**, Côtes de Castillon, Bordeaux, France (**Wai**). Public enemy number one has always been inexpensive red Bordeaux. We all know that the top Châteaux make amazing wines, but under a tenner your chances of finding any joy are slightly dodgier than winning Euro Millions! Well here is the wine that puts all others to shame, and it is a ripsnorter. Packed with briary, dense, velvety fruit and coming from the baking hot 2003 vintage, this is one of the best-value red Bordeaux I have ever tasted. Run to the shops now!

£8.20 **Vega Real Tinto, 2003**, Ribera del Duero, Spain (**Jeroboams & Laytons**). Smarty pants Ribera del Duero costs a bomb. This wine doesn't. I am not sure why because it tastes brilliant and the Tempranillo strawberry and cherry fruit is perfectly augmented with fine oak and crunchy tannins. I am at a loss to explain this anomaly. Not to worry, though, I am sure you will take advantage of the situation.

£8.35 **Bourgueil, Cuvée des Pins, Domaine de la Lande, 2003**, Loire, France (**Haynes, Hanson &**

MEDIUM-WEIGHT

Clarke). Cabernet Franc is one of the most underrated red grapes in the world. It forms the backbone of Château Cheval Blanc, St Emilion, Bordeaux – the 1947 was the greatest red wine I have ever tasted – but the place where it is grown and rarely blended is not Bordeaux but the Loire Valley. Here estates like Domaine de la Lande handcraft staggeringly serious wines. Cheap as chips, heaven knows why. These guys make epic reds and in a vintage like 2003, which was the warmest on record, they made unmissable cuvées. For a lot less than a tenner you can reward your palate with this incredible wine – decant it and the medium-weight violet and mulberry fruit will invade your olfactory system, and hopefully never leave.

£8.98 **Asda Extra Special Rioja, 2001**, Spain (**Asd**). I am sworn to secrecy about the origins of this wine, but I can assure you it is from the very top drawer. This Rioja is worth every bit of the £8.98. And when I tell you that there will be a Christmas promotion in which the price will drop to £6.98, you'll have to make a diary date for this wine. You heard it here first!

£8.99 **Fitou Les Quatre, 2003**, Mont Tauch, France (**Wai**). Coming from fifty-year-old vines and made from Carignan, Grenache and Syrah, this is one of the finest Fitous I can remember. It is liquid crushed-velvet, bound around summer pudding fruit and smart, seasoned oak. Perfect.

£8.99 **Katnook Founders Block Cabernet Sauvignon, 2002**, Coonawarra, South Australia

(**Bibendum**, **Off the Vine** and **Odd**). Katnook has recently introduced this epic second label wine andit embodies all of the class, style and breeding of the flagship label, only at a more affordable price. The exciting, blackcurrant-imbued Coonawarra Cab fruit is really rocking in Founders, and it just shows how important Cabernet is in Australia. There is serious complexity here – I know you'll love this wine.

£8.99 **Rasteau Préstige, Domaine des Coteaux de Travers, 2003**, Southern Rhône, France (**Boo**). Meaty southern Rhône reds that taste like Châteauneuf-du-Pape but which cost half the price are very welcome in my Top 250. Just starting to open up and show terrific blackberry, lavender, thyme and leather notes, this is going to be a winter 2005/6 favourite for stews and hotpots. Decant it, stick your nose in the top and savour the scent of garrigue (the wild hedgerows and rocky terrain of the warm southern Rhône and Provence).

£8.99 **Rosso di Montepulciano, Poliziano, 2004**, Tuscany, Italy (**Boo** and **Sai**). This wine is a perfect example of the simply brilliant winemaking at Poliziano. The fact that the Rosso is still well under a tenner (when their competitors' wines have long since passed that mark) is testament to their hard work and respect for their loyal fans. The red cherry, fresh herb and dark chocolate flavours evoke the true taste of Tuscany in a glass. Don't miss out on this wine – it is very smart indeed. Make sure you decant it to release the full array of flavours.

MEDIUM-WEIGHT

£9.99 **Kangarilla Road Shiraz, 2003**, McLaren Vale, South Australia (**Maj**). Kevin and Helen O'Brien are the coolest of couples. On my annual visit to McLaren Vale I make sure we have a drink, because I always end up laughing my head off and getting into mischief. Their recent releases are the first to make the grade for the Top 250. In fact, I wish I had room to list more. This beautifully balanced Shiraz is designed to be drunk now, willingly releasing its full array of berry and spice fruit without even having to be coaxed out of the glass, but stocks move fast so get in quick. The sister wine is a 2004 Kangarilla Road Viognier (£9.99, **Maj**), which also sings high-note peach and lemon balm from the moment it is poured. Turn the music up and get a bottle of each ready – let Kevin and Helen entertain you!

£9.99 **Tim Adams Fergus, 2002**, Clare Valley, South Australia (**Tes**). Fergus is one of the most complete wines on the shelves today. A totally focused aroma of cranberry, red plum and wild cherry leaps out of the glass and the palate then drives forward with meaty, darker fruit. Sealed in a screwcap and eminently age-worthy (if you can keep your hands on it), this is a very special wine. My respect for Fergus stems from the fact that it is a Grenache-based wine but it doesn't have scary alcohol, and this means it is truly Olympic when matching to food. If it's meat or cheese, it works. Another wine worth mentioning from the once-in-a-lifetime 2002 vintage is 2002 Tim Adams Aberfeldy Shiraz (£19.99, **Australian Wine Club** and **Oz Wines**). My advice is to buy it, keep it and in ten years savour every drop!

MEDIUM-WEIGHT

£10.99 **Hegarty Chamans, Cuvée 1, 2003**,
Minervois, Languedoc, France (**Adnams**). This
beautiful wine, made from Syrah, Carignan and
Mourvèdre, has just hit the UK market. Made to
exacting standards and possessing dense, dark,
mineral- and garrigue-scented fruit, one hour in a
decanter is all that is needed to turn it into a full-on,
all-singing and dancing cabaret star. As the fruit
gradually emerges from its straitjacket, it loses its
inhibitions and becomes refreshingly carnal.

£11.00 **Domaine Bunan Bandol, 2001**, Provence,
France (**M&S**). This is a true slice of Provence,
brimming with funky Mourvèdre, Cinsault,
Grenache and Syrah. Old vines and traditional
winemaking make for a truffle- and sweet-leather-
scented, black-fruit stuffed wine. Drink with wild
boar or venison.

£11.49 **Peter Lehmann Light Pass Cabernet
Sauvignon, 2002**, Barossa Valley, South
Australia (**Odd**). A brand new wine to the UK –
once again, I was the first to see this stunner. Peter
Lehmann is widely regarded as a Shiraz expert, but
when a cool vintage like 2002 comes along, it is
worth sniffing out Cabernets, too. Light Pass, made
by Andrew Wigan, one of the most delightful men
in the wine world, is a genuine, future classic. With
finely chiselled features, a linear, long, erudite palate
and a textbook cassis and fine mint leaf nose, this is
a sensational wine. I have opened it for French,
Californian and Chilean wine experts, and they all
marvelled at the class and value in the glass.

MEDIUM-WEIGHT

£11.99 **Boycat Merlot by Linda Domas, 2004**,
McLaren Vale, South Australia (**Bedales** and **Novum**).
I have tasted this no less than ten times and on every
occasion I am reminded just how extraordinary the
flavours are. I keep expecting them to change,
mellow, transmogrify, but I am delighted to report
they don't. So here we go – this is the most bizarre,
palate-bogglingly extraterrestrial wine in this book.
The sheer concentration of fruit, which abounds with
plum, green tea, briar, mulberry, liquorice, warm pitch,
blueberry ice cream, sweet soy sauce and violets, is
staggering. Merlot? Not as we know it, Captain.

£11.99 **St-Joseph, Les Vins de Vienne, 2003**,
Northern Rhône, France (**Maj**). With exceedingly
smart parentage (the three musketeers – Gaillard,
Cuilleron and Villard), the Vins de Vienne wines are
very serious offerings indeed. This Syrah, from
impeccably sourced fruit, is frighteningly self-
assured. With benchmark pepper, iodine, pastrami,
clove, blackberry and black-cherry fruit coursing
across your palate, you may need a moment to
gather your senses because there is so much going
on. Have a seat, serve up some senior-quality cheese,
top-flight charcuterie, cornichons (those tricky little
French gherkins) and sourdough bread, and put the
cutlery away. This is posh peasant food and the wine
is as bucolic and Dumas-esque as you can get.

£12.50 **Château Perron, 2002**, Lalande de Pomerol,
Bordeaux, France (**Lea & Sandeman**). I wait all year
to find a red Bordeaux like this, so thank goodness
it turned up just before the deadline. The balance

MEDIUM-WEIGHT

red 73

between the authenticity of raw materials and the modernity of winemaking in Perron is sensational. Ripe and complex, with pristine oak and fine tannins, this is a very accomplished piece of craftsmanship. Any claret lover would be amazed at the depth of fruit and length of aftertaste on this delicious wine.

£12.55 **Chorey-lès-Beaune, Maison Champy, 2002**, Burgundy, France (**Haynes, Hanson & Clark**). Champy has raised its game so much and in such a short period of time that I am delighted to include this in the Top 250. With dark-cherry fruit and a lick of spice, it is a fantastic, ballsy, new-style red Burgundy, and the sort of wine that you should open to impress the parents of a new girl/boyfriend!

£12.99 **Château Cambon La Pelouse, 2003**, Haut-Médoc, Bordeaux, France (**Wai**). This was one of the very best Haut-Médoc 2003s and it has just arrived in this country. Richer than you might expect and remarkably forward, this is a superb Bordeaux, and perfect for roast beef and Yorkshire pud.

£13.50 **Crozes-Hermitage, Domaine Alain Graillot, 2003**, Northern Rhône, France (**Yapp**). Oh my God! Graillot's 2003 Crozes is a stunner. Jason Yapp has kept back some cases especially for readers of *The Wine List*. So, here is a very short, one-line tasting note that will be guaranteed to make you order some bottles: 'If you don't order it all, I will!'

£13.99 **De Bortoli Reserve Pinot Noir, 2003**, Yarra Valley, Victoria, Australia (**Odd and

MEDIUM-WEIGHT

R.S. Wines). Beautiful, organza- and tuille-wearing lusciousness in a glass – this is a wine you'll want to dance with, not just open, welcome and introduce to your friends. Silky, voluptuous, wild-cherry fruit, with all the accompanying upholstery, knobs and twiddles, how can this cost only £13.99? Steve Webber makes great wine and this is a stunner.

£13.99 **Turkey Flat Butcher's Block, 2003**, Barossa Valley, South Australia (**Edencroft**, **Fine & Rare**, **Halifax**, **Harrods**, **Martinez**, **Portland** and **Sommelier**). 2003 Butcher's starts off as a mild-mannered, beautifully balanced, complex red blend in the glass, and then it effortlessly and silently changes into a Châteauneuf-du-Pape-bashing berserker. The depth of fruit, albeit in a remarkably restrained manner, is incredible in this wine. At no stage does it raise its voice, only murmuring in a fearsome Christopher Walken way about just how delighted your taste buds are going to be when you drink this wine. And believe it, it's true!

£14.99 **Wither Hills Pinot Noir, 2004**, Marlborough, South Island, New Zealand (**Ballantynes**, **Decorum**, **Michael Jobling**, **Odd**, **Old Forge**, **Simon Charles**, **Sommelier**, **Villeneuve**, **Wai**, **Wicked** and **Wine Society**). Made by one of the hottest winemaking teams in the southern hemisphere, 2004 Wither Hills Pinot is, dare I whisper it, even better than the multi-award-winning 2003. I was privileged to have a guided tour around the brand new Wither Hills winery and visitor centre during its final few months of

MEDIUM-WEIGHT

construction last year, and was privy to a very special tasting indeed. Brent Marris and Ben Glover showed me the barrel components of this wine and let slip a few trade secrets. Suffice to say their attention to detail and incredible knowledge of their vineyards is nothing short of inspirational. These guys will no doubt gather even more people into their already crowded fan base thanks to the majesty in this glass. WH Pinot is shiny plums, wild cherries, Turkish Delight and a Bentley Continental Flying Spur all rolled into one.

£15.00 **Parker Terra Rossa Cabernet Sauvignon, 2001**, Coonawarra, South Australia (**Corney & Barrow**). With very intense fruit, highly tuned oak and a supercharged finish, this is everything you'd want from a Parker Cabernet – except that it is half the price you'd usually shell out for the pleasure! You will need to decant this wine, cook the smartest joint of beef you can find and take Monday off work – that is how good this wine is.

£16.50 **Stonier Reserve Pinot Noir, 2003**, Mornington Peninsula, Victoria, Australia (**Bibendum** and **The Cellar Door**). I tasted this wine in its infancy, out of the barrel, and I thought it would turn out to be winemaker Geraldine McFaul's *pièce de résistance*. Firm, grown-up, confident and masterful, this Pinot takes control of your olfactory system and systematically ticks off all of the hallmark aroma and flavour boxes. The colour is not unlike youthful Barbera, it is so amazing, and the punchy plum theme keeps you guessing until the end – a wondrous wine.

MEDIUM-WEIGHT

£16.95 **Seghesio Barbera, 2003**, North Coast, California (**George Hill**, **Liberty**, **Valvona & Crolla**, **Villeneuve**, **Wine Raks** and **Noel Young**). My tasting with Camille Seghesio earlier this year was amazing. Every bottle opened was terrific. But my pick of the lot was this Barbera and the 2003 Sonoma County Zinfandel (£14.49, **Bennetts**, **Boo**, **Harrods**, **Liberty**, **Selfridges** and **Villeneuve**). Both wines are screwcapped and both wines show extraordinary fruit purity and drive in the glass. The Barbera is world class and the Zin, which is what these guys specialise in, is utterly stunning. Both wines also share a density and colour that is luxury in a glass. The Barbera is blueberry driven and the Zin walks on the prune/mulberry side of the street. Whichever you choose, you will be guaranteed to be wearing a smile that will last a week by the end of the bottle!

£19.95 **Carrick Estate Pinot Noir, 2003**, Central Otago, South Island, New Zealand (**deFINE**, **Great Western**, **Playford**, **Villeneuve** and **Wadebridge**). I loved the 2002 PN from Carrick and it narrowly missed out on a slot in last year's Top 250. Not to worry, though, because this 2003 is even better. This is a more masculine style of Pinot than you might expect from Otago, with plenty of brooding blackberry power and depth. Carrick is one of the founding fathers of the region and their entire portfolio of wines is a joy – ask the merchants listed for a rundown on their stocks.

£22.50 **Mount Edward Pinot Noir, 2003**, Central Otago, South Island, New Zealand (**Jeroboams &**

MEDIUM-WEIGHT

Laytons). Over the last five or so years Central Otago has amassed some serious world street cred for its top flight Pinot Noirs. But not everything is as it seems. In reality, there is a hard core of producers who strive to make the finest wines they can and a separate bunch of Johnny Come Latelys who are foisting sub-standard versions of this grape on us at frightening prices. A mate of mine suggested that the majority of these nouveau Pinot pretenders are people who decided to downshift from their previously successful corporate careers and retire, making wine in one of the most beautiful wine regions in the world. Who wouldn't want to? The problem is that making wine, let alone the Holy Grail of wine, Pinot Noir, is not downshifting. It is like saying I am going to take it easy from now on and design helicopters for a living. It can't be done! *Caveat emptor* – the list of the best NZ producers is in my gazetteer. Mount Edward is one of the good guys. With tight, grainy, dense, powerful, dark-berry fruit, this wine shows the true potential of Otago's hallowed soil and climate. This is a sensational wine but you must be patient – it will not hit its true form for another two or three years.

● ●

£5.49 **Casillero del Diablo Cabernet Sauvignon, 2004**, Maipo Valley, Chile (**Asd**, **Boo**, **Mor**, **Odd**, **Sai**, **Som**, **Tes**, **Thr** and **Wai**). Can you believe it? Marcelo Papa makes nine million bottles of this wine every year. So, not only is it the best-value Cabernet on the planet, it is also the easiest to find on the shelves. I have no idea how he captures so much class, intensity, depth of blackcurrant fruit and style in this wine for only a fiver, but I am not complaining. This is the definitive 'bring a bottle' wine for a party. It doesn't cost much, you won't mind leaving it behind and, if it's opened, you'll be delighted to drink a glass. The entire family of 'Devil's Cellar' wines is phenomenal, but my favoured second pick this year is the 2004 CdD Shiraz (£5.49, **Asd**, **Maj**, **Odd**, **Sai**, **Som** and **Thr**). It is another wonderful wine, with less overt power and more spice and red fruit aromas than the Cabernet.

£6.49 **Concha y Toro Winemaker's Lot 137 Malbec, 2004**, Cachapoal, Chile (**Odd**). This is what Marcelo Papa does when he is having fun. The Winemaker's Lot series includes the frighteningly serious 2004 Winemaker's Lot 401 Syrah (£6.99, **Odd**) and 2004 Winemaker's Lot 159 Cabernet (£9.99, **Odd**). Add these two stunners to the ridiculously inexpensive Malbec and you have one of the most impressive families of wines on the shelves today. Over the last few years I have been privy to the tweaking that Marcelo has done to improve the portfolio year on year. The result is – best ever releases. The 2004s are simply incredible.

£6.99 **Château Cazal Viel, Cuvée des Fées, 2003**, St-Chinian, Languedoc, France (**Wai**). This is a rampantly impressive Syrah/Viognier blend that shows just about everyone how it's done. The extraordinary thing is that there is no oak whatsoever used in this wine. It is massive, brooding,

BLOCKBUSTER

inky, almost menacing – and I love every single drop in the bottle. If you are remotely serious about wine, do not miss Cuvée des Fées.

£6.99 **Porcupine Ridge Syrah, 2004**, Coastal Region, South Africa (**Wai**). This wine carries on an unbroken run of excellence for Porky Pie Syrah. In fact, it is the best vintage yet. Sealed with a screwcap at last, and bursting with unbridled briary, curranty and peppery nuances, Côtes-du-Rhône simply can't keep up with the pace that this epic wine sets.

£6.99 **Ravenswood Vintners Blend Zinfandel, 2003**, California (**Asd**, **Maj**, **Mor**, **Christopher Piper**, **Som**, **Tes**, **Thr**, **Wai** and **Wine Society**). The new vintage of Vintners Blend is due into the shops at any moment and it is stunning. This is one of California's most reliable and impressive wines and, taking price into account, it is easily at the top of the ladder. The dark-plum, blueberry, vanilla, chocolate, blackberry and sweet-cinnamon spice notes are spectacular in this wine. If you love Vintners blend but want to open the throttle a touch and trade up to one of the more serious Ravenswood wines, then track down a bottle of the 2002 Lodi Old Vine Zinfandel (£7.99, **Sai**). Lodi has clearly been working out because the muscle and definition of this beauty is a wonder to behold. If you are cooking a serious piece of steak, employ the services of this wine to help you wash it down.

£6.99 **Rutherglen Estate Durif, 2004**, Rutherglen, Victoria, Australia (**Wai** and **Wine Society**). This wine has made the Top 250 before and I have no doubt it will make it again. Why? Because there are very few wines as glossy, slick, purple and plummy on the planet, and this makes it the ideal partner to crispy aromatic duck and heavily sauced barbecued beef. Fabulous value and unashamedly tongue in cheek (I think?) – this is a cracker.

£7.49 **Orobio, Artadi, 2003**, Rioja, Spain (**Odd**). I adore the wines from Artadi, and most of them are so expensive they are way out of my league. But this heroic little chap is a chip off the old block and it has all of the style and pizzazz of some of its starrier siblings. Punchy, dark, brooding and blessed with dense, dark fruit this is a muscular little sod, and it makes for very exciting drinking. Make sure you cook something suitably Pagan.

£7.95 **Heartland Shiraz, 2004**, South Australia (**Abbey, Ballantynes, deFINE, Execellars, Great Western, Nidderdale, Odd, Oz Wines, Playford** and **Noel Young**). Ben Glaetzer's entry-level Shiraz is really rocking in the 2003 vintage. With serious fruit quality and enough mint, eucalyptus and smart oak to impress, you must find this wine. The 2003 will be around in all of the above stores until the end of 2005. But I can't wait for the 2004 to arrive on the shelves. As every year goes by, Ben learns more about his vineyards and his consumers – he visits the UK and conducts more tastings each year than virtually any other Aussie winemaker. This is paying off, because 2004 Heartland is very yummy indeed and his fans will lap it up.

BLOCKBUSTER

£7.99 **Diemersfontein Pinotage, 2005**, Wellington, South Africa (**Asd** and **Wai**). The 2005 vintage of Diemers' beast-like Pinotage is the best ever. A tank sample, back in May, knocked me off my feet. Fans of this wine, and it sells out very quickly when it hits the shelves in the autumn, will revel in the bravado, intensity and flamboyance of this stunning dark, swarthy, coffee and mocha fruit.

£7.99 **Wakefield Estate Shiraz, 2004**, Clare Valley, South Australia (**Odd**, **Som**, **Sommelier** and **Unw**). The dark, deep, chocolate and plumcake fruit is sumptuously appointed in this innocently (read boringly) labelled bottle. Not giving much away on the outside, the contents speak volumes. This is one find that you may want to keep to yourself, as it is not only the best Wakefield Estate Shiraz I have ever tried, but it is also screwcap sealed, so it wears its very own guarantee of perfection, too.

£8.49 **Monferrato Rosso, Le Monache, Michele Chiarlo, 2003**, Monferrato, Italy (**Odd**). This is a mighty glass of red wine and one that is positively brimming with liquorice, plums and cherries. You will need a prodigious carnivorous dish to offset the power in this grand wine.

£8.95 **Côtes-du-Rhône Villages, Domaine de la Jérome, 2003**, Sylvette Bréchet, Southern Rhône, France (**Jeroboams & Laytons**). Regardless of price, this is the most impressive red Rhône I have tasted this year. It is utterly fantastic. I wrote 'phenomenal, awesome, tremendous and staggering'

BLOCKBUSTER

in my tasting notes. So what does it taste like? Remember how warm it was in the summer of 2003? Well, that heat ripened these grapes like never before, and the intensity of black, briary, plum, berry and sweet oak spices is what makes this wine so impressive. If you have the cash I would buy a case – it is not going to do anything other than improve over the next five years.

£8.95 **Montepulciano d'Abruzzo, Valle Reale, 2002**, Marche, Italy (**ten-acre**). Brian Peacock has a well-honed palate and he completely blew me away with his stunning Montepulciano. To be honest, I thought the price would be nearer £15 on first sniff, such is the class and complexity of this divine red wine. The dark, spicy fruit seems to attack the palate with some aggression and intent, but what really happens is it gives your taste buds a big hug instead. The powerful presence but genial mood makes for a superbly engaging experience. Give Brian a buzz at ten-acre – he has a cornucopia of rare gems on his list.

£8.99 **Brunato Vineyards Shiraz by Linda Domas, 2004**, McLaren Vale, South Australia (**Odd**). Chunky, honest, bright and affable, this is a fabulous slice of fantastic, old-vine McLaren Vale Shiraz, and it is sold for a fraction of its true worth. It is also nice that Steve Brunato's name sits alongside winemaker Linda's on the label, because he is the grape-growing half of their partnership, and these guys (a bit like goalkeepers) rarely get the plaudits, even when the team plays a blinder. There is a handmade feel to these wines, probably because they *are* handmade, so remember this when you have the choice between a Linda Domas wine and something else made by the thousands of cases. It is the vinous equivalent of farmers' market produce – stunning quality, authentic and grown with care. Flick back to the rosé section and you'll see Linda's Shotbull, and the 2003 Shotbull Shiraz (£9.99, **Odd**) is the red version of this wine – try it if you dare!

£8.99 **d'Arenberg Custodian Grenache, 2002**, McLaren Vale, South Australia (**Bibendum**, **Boo**, **Jolly Vintner**, **Odd** and **Wine Society**). '02 Custodian is a Vivienne Westwood creation. It parades its decadent, Regency glamour with aplomb, sporting a pompadour quiff, but carrying a flick-knife up its sleeve. If you have ever seen the hysterical highwayman movie *Plunkett and Maclean*, starring Robert Carlyle and Johnny Lee Miller, this is the wine that must have inspired the costumes, the music, the mood and the humour. With outlandish flavours popping in and out of the glass like the cameo performances by Alan Cumming, Michael Gambon and Ken Stott, this is a totally enjoyable romp. Buy the DVD and drink this wine from start to finish and then try to tell me Dick Turpin wasn't one of the coolest blokes that ever lived.

£8.99 **The Storm, Reserve Sangiovese/Merlot, 2004**, South Africa (**Thr**). A beautiful wild cherry aroma, with raw, tangy edges of liquorice root and mint leaf around a central abyss of opaque black fruit. What happens next? Do you walk into the eye of the storm?

BLOCKBUSTER

£9.99 **McManis Family Vineyards Cabernet Sauvignon, 2003**, California (**Coo**). With mighty blackberry fruit, abundant sweet clove and cinnamon spice, and wondrous vanilla and woodsmoke elements clawing their way into the palate action, this is a great Cabernet and one that will be splendid with a good old homemade burger and fat chips.

£9.99 **Penfold's Bin 28 Kalimna Shiraz, 2002**, Barossa Valley, South Australia (**Maj**, **Som**, **Sommelier**, **Tes** and **Thr**). This wine is one of Australia's unsung heroes and I challenge anyone in the world (and beyond) to build another such immediately appealing, yet eminently age-worthy Shiraz. It can't be done, can it? I have stood in the Kalimna vineyard and it looks like a Star Wars set – otherworldly, gnarled, tree-like plants from a different solar system shamble around this place at night. I was told they were ancient Shiraz vines, but I didn't believe my guide. Regardless, this is the best Kalimna I have ever tasted, and you must find it. On this planet it is known as the awesome 2002 vintage. On Naboo in the Outer Rim Territories they call it the 8#63513g.

£9.99 **Vidal Syrah, 2003**, Hawke's Bay, North Island, New Zealand (**Luvians**, **Vicki's** and **Wimbledon**). Rod McDonald has a very perceptive palate and it is a gift that he employs to great effect when making his wines. This Syrah, which is grown in the prime Gimblett Gravels sub-region, could be meaty and muscular and overbearing, but he has calmed it down, preferring to show earthy characteristics and fruit complexity. Syrah is only just finding its feet in

BLOCKBUSTER

NZ, but the style (somewhere between the Rhône and coolish Aussie regions) is looking very attractive. This is a delicious wine that is mellow enough to attack now.

£10.99 **Clos de los Siete, 2004**, Tunuyan, Argentina (**Maj, Odd** and **Wai Canary Wharf branch**). TWL'05 was the first to write up the 2003 Clos de los Siete last year and I was the first in the UK to taste a preview bottle of this heroic 2004 back in May. This wine is so impressive that in the space of just two vintages I feel it is now setting the standard for all other serious South American red blends. There is so much structure and intensity here – but it is in no way too big or too filling. The fruit is pristine, with impossibly dark plum, loganberry and chocolate notes flooding out of the glass. The oak is exceptionally attractive, too – all toasty charcoal embers and Far Eastern spices. Made from a blend of Malbec, Merlot, Syrah and Cabernet, I shudder to say it but the rest of the New World should sit up and take note of this wine, its price and its message. This is a mighty wine and it deserves a mighty following.

£11.49 **Heritage Shiraz, 2003**, Barossa Valley, South Australia (**Australian Wine Club** and **Sommelier**). Steve Hoff has put away his tutu and got back into his trademark shorts and T-shirt. The 2003 Heritage Shiraz is a stormer – crammed with wild mulberry and blueberry fruit, dusted with an aroma of serious pastrami and cracked pepper, and blessed with stunning acidity that cleanses, balances and refreshes the palate between sips. Neither too alcoholic nor too oaky, this is a tremendous wine which confirms everyone's belief that Steve is a genius despite his insistence that he's just an ordinary guy.

£11.99 **Peter Lehmann Futures Shiraz, 2003**, Barossa Valley, South Australia (**Boo**, **D Byrne**, **Cheers**, **George Hill**, **Nidderdale**, **Odd**, **Oxford**, **Portland** and **Whittalls**). 'Wigs' (Andrew Wigan) has further improved on the already awe-inspiring Futures recipe and has made a devastatingly impressive wine out of the 2003. This is one for the cellar, but it's a guaranteed blue-chip investment.

£12.49 **Fox Gordon Eight Uncles Shiraz, 2003**, Barossa Valley, South Australia (**Odd** and **Vin du Van**). Tash Mooney spends all day working for a massive Aussie wine company, making something out of nothing, and then, at the end of the day, she goes home and exercises her fine touch and exceptional palate on her very own label, Fox Gordon. She is one of Australia's most prodigious talents so pick up Eight Uncles, you better hurry, and then marvel at the kaleidoscopic beauty in the glass. If this wine makes you as wistful, imaginative and dreamy as it does me, then look out for her two other cuvées – 2003 King Louis Cabernet and 2003 Hannah's Swing Shiraz (£18.99, **Four Walls**, **Odd** and **Vin du Van**) – they build on her theme of layering flavour upon flavour upon flavour – astonishing.

£13.99 **De Bortoli Estate Shiraz/Viognier, 2003**, Yarra Valley, Victoria, Australia (**Odd** and **RS Wines**). This is one of the finest of the new wave of S/V

BLOCKBUSTER

blends, and it's one of the rare examples that doesn't pulverise your wallet. Steve Webber has an Old World palate and this wine is fashioned for the globetrotting wine lover. Smooth, savoury, black fruit and pepper stuffed, and ever so genial – that's both Steve and the wine!

£14.99 **Knappstein Single Vineyard Enterprise Cabernet, 2002**, Clare Valley, South Australia (**Bibendum**, **Odd** and **Off the Vine**). Errol Flynn in a glass! This is a handsome, daring, swashbuckling wine, with a superb nose, fine, elegant fruit and a long, laid-back finish. Blockbuster, yes, but Enterprise delivers its message by whispering charmingly in your ear rather than shouting through a megaphone inches from your face. It will charm the pants off you, so watch out! Once tasted, never forgotten, the blackcurrant fruit in this wine is truly delicious and the overall feeling after drinking a glass or two of this wine is that you have been well and truly ravished.

£14.99 **Villa Maria Reserve Cabernet/Merlot, 2002**, Hawke's Bay, North Island, New Zealand (**Luvians**, **Vicki's** and **Wimbledon**). Epic vintage, sensational quality fruit, screwcapped and just about coming into its drinking zone, this company is blazing a very smart trail with almost all of its grape varieties, and this Cab/Merlot is no exception. It wasn't that long ago that we thought whites were all that would emerge from NZ. With intensely perfumed, elegantly oaked blockbusters like this on the shelves, California, Chile, Argentina, Italy, Australia and France must all be on their toes.

mountain on *wheels*

£16.00 **Rijk's, Private Cellar Pinotage, 2002**,
Tulbagh, South Africa (**Great Northern**, **Great Western** and **Simon Charles**). There are very few wines with the gloss and sheen that this black monster has in the glass. With a nose of espresso coffee beans and wickedly dark chocolate sauce and prunes, this is a veritable mountain on wheels. The wondrous thing about Rijk's Pinotage is that on the palate it is not remotely as terrifying – a Hagrid! In fact, the finish is as silky and smooth as can be.

£16.99 **Jack & Knox, The Outsider Shiraz, 2004**,
Western Cape, South Africa (**deFINE**, **Harrogate** and **Veritas**). 2002 Outsider was one of the most remarkable wines I had ever tasted – regal, intense, all-encompassing, bludgeoning my system into compliance. The 2004 is better. In fact, it is totally awesome – brilliant depth, heroic length and mighty finish. You have to be fit and able even to get the cork out, let alone heft the weight of this bottle. Put it near your nose and you are a superhero, taste it and you are The Outsider.

£18.99 **Wolf Blass Grey Label Shiraz, 2002**, South Australia (**FGL Wine Estates tel. 020 8843 8411**). I reckon that this first-class Barossa/ Clare/McLaren Vale blend is a definitive Blass wine. They do this challenging 'wine-building' exercise very, very well. The object of the exercise is to capture more complexity in the finished wine than there is in any of the component parts. With this in mind – Wolfy achieves and surpasses their aim with room to spare.

BLOCKBUSTER

£22.50 **d'Arenberg Ironstone Pressings, 2002**, McLaren Vale, South Australia (**Bibendum**, **The Cellar Door**, **Cellar Door Wines**, **Odd**, **Wai** and **Wine Society**). Big statement time – this is the highest scoring wine I have ever tasted from d'Arenberg. Ironstone is a 70% Grenache, 25% Shiraz, 5% Mourvèdre blend and it is sublime. Buy every bottle you find before that American bloke scores it and the price shoots through the roof. What does it taste like? A world of red-wine flavours in one glass.

£22.95 **Godolphin by Ben Glaetzer, 2004**, Barossa Valley, South Australia (**Abbey**, **Michael Jobling**, **Great Northern**, **Great Western**, **Nidderdale**, **Playford**, **SWIG** and **Noel Young**). This is the earth-shatteringly brilliant younger brother to Amon-Ra (a nose-bleedingly expensive monolith), and it's a hedonistic Shiraz/ Cabernet blend. Where Amon-Ra is, admittedly, completely over the top (not remotely my scene), Godolphin is near perfection. This is one of the most highly anticipated launches of the year – it is due in store in the autumn. I first tasted this wine (sworn to secrecy about its name, the blend and even its existence) back in February. I nearly had to lie down in a dark room for an hour, such was its effect on my system. I adore Godolphin and I defy anyone not to be struck dumb by its flavour impact. It is certainly worth every bit of the £23. So, for a white-knuckle experience, do your best to find a bottle of this wine.

£24.00 **Yering Station Reserve Shiraz/Viognier, 2003**, Yarra Valley, Victoria (**Maj Fine Wine**, **Wai**

BLOCKBUSTER

Canary Wharf and **Wimbledon Wine**). With less Viognier added than the 2002, and more fire in its belly and edge on the palate, this is the wine that puts Yering on the world stage. Step up to the spotlight, you belong there.

£24.99 **Penfold's St Henri Shiraz, 2001**, Barossa Valley, South Australia (**Berry Bros.**, **Sommelier** and **Wine Society**). Extraordinary complexity and (please forgive me) a ridiculously small price tag for the cosmic goings on in this wine. It always sounds ridiculous to say that something that costs £25 is a bargain, but this is one of the world's most important Syrahs and, thank God, it is relatively accessible to us mere mortals.

£39.99 **Yalumba Octavius Shiraz, 2001**, Barossa Valley, South Australia (**Fine & Rare**, **Harrods**, **Jeroboams & Laytons**, **Veritas** and **Vin du Van**). Octavius has always been a smart wine but in 2001 (a cosmic vintage) it truly delivers – single-minded, almost obsessive dedication to rewarding the drinker with fantastic, broad brush strokes of flavour, without losing its footing. It works. Due in stores from October, this is one of those wines that any wine lover who has truly been bitten by the bug would love as a Christmas pressie.

£39.99 **Penfold's RWT Shiraz, 2002**, Barossa Valley, South Australia (**Berry Bros.**, **Farr**, **Fortnum & Mason**, **Harrods**, **Selfridges**, **Sommelier**, **Wai**, **Wine Society** and **Noel Young**). I never thought that RWT could look so polished and controlled. Caution! DO

NOT APPROACH – this is a cold-blooded assassin, and you will be compromised in a moment. The 2002 vintage, with its control, attitude, iron will and deft Matrix moves, makes Red Wine Trial one of the most compelling and unnerving wines of the year.

● ●

£4.99 half bottle, **Moscato d'Asti, Nivole, Michele Chiarlo, 2004**, Piedmont, Italy (**Boo** and **Odd**). This is the Dinky toy of the fizzy sweet world and I love it. I'd serve my guests a bottle each, but I suppose if you are particularly abstemious you could stretch a half bottle to four glasses. Chill it down icy cold and then watch your guests grin like idiots when the first whoosh of tingly grape juice hits their larynx. Adult soda pop? Of course it is, but we can't let the kids have all the fun can we?

£5.99 **Brown Brothers Late Harvested Muscat, 2004**, Victoria, Australia (**Boo** and **Mor**). Forget that this wine only costs a mere £1 per glass. Don't be a snob! Just buy it and then pick your jaw off the floor. This 'full' bottle would easily do ten glasses at a dinner party, which makes it one of the finest-value sweet wines in the known universe. A regular Top 250 candidate, this is the definitive grapey Muscat, and the French, with the famous Muscat de Beaumes-de-Venise, can't do this class or precision for twice or even three times the money.

£5.99 **Brown Brothers Moscato, 2004**, South Eastern Australia (**Tes**). This joyous, five-and-a-half per cent alcohol Muscat is an essential wine in your armoury. Imagine crushing ice-cold grapes and then jetting a soda siphon through them. This energetic explosion of frothy, fruity grape juice is the result. Drink it as a nerve-jangling, futuristic aperitif or with fresh fruit puddings. The 2005 arrives around Christmas and it will be just as jolly.

£5.99 50cl bottle, **Pirramimma Late Harvest Riesling, 1999**, McLaren Vale, South Australia (**Maj**). Gosh, this is a fabulous scoop! I first tasted this wine in March and the guys at Pirramimma sadly informed me that Majestic were not going to take it. Boo hiss. I tried again later in the year and they had miraculously changed their minds. Yippee! We can now feast on this six-year-old, fully mature, wildly exotic wine. This is a half-litre bot and it will go a long way at a party. It will also go perfectly with Ben and Jerry's Vanilla Caramel Fudge.

£5.99 half bottle, **Robertson Winery, Almond Grove Noble Late Harvest Weisser Riesling, 2003**, Robertson, South Africa (**Maj**). Hold on to your hat because this wine is a whirlwind of flavour. The orange marmalade and dribbly honey core erupts from the glass in all directions. You will spot toffee, coconut, pineapple, Golden Syrup, candied peel and goodness knows what else in your glass. I think this is one of the most unexpected and yet fascinatingly lush wines of the year.

£6.00 half bottle, **Château Bel-Air, 2002**, Sainte-Croix du Mont, Bordeaux, France (**Haynes, Hanson &**

Clark). Also available In full bottles, this is one of the most delicious, light, fragrant, sun-kissed wines I have found this year. Pale honey coloured, with the merest whisper of fresh meadow flowers and mild, breakfast fruit salad nuances, this is the perfect accompaniment to fresh fruit puddings and, at the front end of a dinner, terrines and pâtés.

£6.99 half bottle, **Peter Lehmann Botrytis Semillon, 2002**, Barossa Valley, South Australia (**Boo**, **Mitchells**, **Odd**, **Portland**, **Theatre of Wine**, **Vin du Van**, **Whittalls** and **Noel Young**). Aussie Semillon is an institution. I always find a botrytised version (the super sweet ones made from rot-effected grapes) because they are so unbelievably gorgeous and rival the best French Sauternes at a fraction of the price. Lehmann's version is smooth, lemony and honeyed, and ever so slightly brandy-snappy. It is a stunner and you could even drink it instead of pud it is so lovely.

£7.95 half bottle, **Woodstock Botrytised Sweet White, 2003**, McLaren Vale, South Australia (**El Vino**, **General Wine**, **Nidderdale**, **Oxford Wine**, **Oz Wines**, **Roberson** and **Wimbledon Wine**). Winemaker Scott Collett is a man mountain and this wine is, admittedly, the antithesis of his character. But real men do drink sweet wine, particularly if your wife makes the greatest mulberry tart on the planet. So thanks Mrs Collett, you have press-ganged him into making a thoroughly delicious sweetie, which hums with juicy melon, honey and orange blossom.

£8.99 50cl bottle, **Domaine de Montahuc, Muscat de Saint Jean de Minervois, 2002**, Languedoc, France (**Odd**). Friendly, silky smooth, grapey and perfect with *tarte au citron*. What more do you need to know? This is the best French Muscat of the year, so it deserves a round of applause.

£10.50 half bottle, **Joostenberg Noble Late Harvest Chenin Blanc, 2004**, Paarl, South Africa (**Berry Bros.**). With an entire fruit bowl of flavour tipped into this sleek little half bottle, this is a remarkably sexy wine. It is not overly sweet, as the acidity in this sumptuous wine helps to keep the palate in check. This means you can drink more of it – hee hee!

£11.99 half bottle, **Château Doisy-Daëne, 2002, Cru Classé, Sauternes**, Bordeaux, France (**Wai**). At twice the price of the Bel-Air and the Peter Lehmann (above), you might not want to step up to this wine. But Doisy-Daëne has something the other two don't, and that is elegance and a lot of breeding. The others have impact and eyebrow-raising flavours. This wine saunters up to you and smooths your furrowed brow. Decide what mood you are in and then pick whichever wine you fancy.

£12.95 50cl bottle, **Coteaux du Layon Beaulieu L'Anclaie, Chateau de Pierre Bise, 2003**, Loire, France (**Lea & Sandeman**). Once in a lifetime a vintage like 2003 comes along and wines that you thought you knew well suddenly grow three heads and turn into something out of a Greek epic. The power, intensity and phenomenal purity of the tropically honeyed fruit is staggering. The only way you'll get your brain around how awesome this wine is, is to try it yourself – I am having trouble putting it into words.

£12.99 half bottle, **Yalumba Botrytised Viognier, 2004**, Wrattonbully, South Australia (**Harrods, Charles Hennings, Hoults, Nidderdale, Philglas, Veritas, The Wine Man** and **Wimbledon**). I was very scared to taste this wine, but it elevated my palate with angelic, peachy flavours and delivered a unique experience that is now the mark by which all others will be judged. Rare, captivating and well worth the hunt.

£14.99 50cl bottle, **Ruppertsberger Riesling Eiswein, 2001**, Pfalz, Germany (**Sai**). It is rare to find vaguely affordable Eiswein. Made from grapes that hang on the vine until Christmas time and freeze in the cold temperatures, these are some of the rarest wines on the planet. The grapes are hand harvested and then crushed in mini wine presses. The juice that comes out is so sweet that you end up with a truly unctuous wine. Fruit cocktail doesn't come close – this is honey, honey and more honey!

£16.95 **Coteaux du Layon Rablay Chateau La Tomaze Cuvée Lys, 1995**, Loire, France (**Yapp**). Here is a wine that should make a sweetie fan pop their cork. Tomaze is a phenomenal producer and this Cuvée Lys is over a decade old. Rare, old Chenin Blanc is one of the most attractive wine styles and, in terms of value for money, this is totally unmissable. Yes, this is a full bottle!

fill your boots

£6.55 **La Gitana Manzanilla, Hidalgo, Sherry, NV**, Spain (**Laymont & Shaw**, **Lay & Wheeler**, **Maj**, **Sai**, **Sommelier**, **Tanners** and **Wai**). Palate-strippingly dry and charged with the early evening responsibility of getting rid of a grotty day's work and realigning your mood for a night's merriment, this Manzanilla does exactly what it is supposed to do. Get some cashews or pistachios to hand and fill your boots.

£6.55 **Waitrose Solera Jerezana Dry Oloroso Sherry, NV**, Spain (**Wai**). Still awesome value for money and desperately over-delivering on style, depth of flavour and authenticity, the Dry Oloroso is my pick of the serious Waitrose sherry bottlings this year. Rich, deep, nutty, tangy, figgy and lingering, get involved with this slice of history.

£6.55 **Waitrose Solera Jerezana Rich Cream Sherry, NV**, Spain (**Wai**). Five years in a row (see Taylor's) this stunning Cream Sherry is a lifetime achievement contender. If you flick through the pudding section of the Food and Wine chapter you will see that everyone needs a bottle of this sherry in their fridge – particularly if you like cakes!

£6.59 50cl bottle, **Sticky Pudding Wine, NV**, Antonio Barbadillo, Sherry, Spain (**Sai**). Made from the bizarre Pedro Ximénez grape, this is a gloopy, super-sweet, sipping wine, reminiscent of liquidised rum-and-raisin ice cream, but with extra rum. It is awesome with Christmas pud or choccies, and you will gawp at the aroma and texture as you sink deeper into the sofa after a huge feast.

£6.99 50cl bottle, **Torres Moscatel Oro, NV**, Catalunya, Spain (**Oxford**, **Roberts & Speight** and **Sai**). This amber-coloured flute of wine is packed with juicy orange blossom, honey, lemon and rosewater-scented fruit. It is silky smooth and would be epic with a *tarte tatin*, sponge pud or any other stalwart winter-warming, fruity crumble. Regardless of its culinary compatibility, this is a stunning wine that is remarkable value and has a heavenly flavour.

£7.99 **Quinta do Portal White Port, NV**, Douro Valley, Portugal (**Great Western**, **Charles Hennings** and **Edward Sheldon**). The burnt honey colour and bizarre Pimms-like sweetness make this one of the sexiest and most intriguing white ports I have ever tasted. The fruit-cocktail notes coupled with a fantastic ginger and spice theme really wow your taste buds, and I reckon that this wine will attract a larger number of takers than a normal red port, particularly at this incredible price. Serve chilled.

£8.49 half bottle, **Emilin Moscatel, Emilio Lustau, NV**, Jerez, Spain (**Connolly's**, **Cooden**, **Flying Corkscrew**, **Fortnum & Mason** and **R.S. Wines**). The sister to the wine below and the super-charged version of the quaint, pretty and innocent Torres wine above, Emilin is a seductive Moscatel. Watch out, because this is no giddy schoolgirl, rather a devastatingly manicured international espionage chick, and she's on a mission.

£8.49 half bottle, **San Emilio PX, Emilio Lustau, NV**, Jerez, Spain (**Ballantynes**, **Bedales**, **Bennetts**,

D. Byrne, Flying Corkscrew, Fortnum & Mason, Luvians, Sommelier, Totnes, and Wright). No other wine comes close to the intensity and impact that San Emilio has on the palate. If you took a sticky pudding wine and reduced it in a pan, eventually you'd have a glass of this nectar. This is PX at its wildest and most brazen. Drink it with, or dribble it over, someone you lust.

£9.99 **Croft Indulgence, NV Port**, Portugal (**Tes**). If you are feeling a little delicate and need a glass of port that will hold your hand, open doors for you, push in your chair and take your coat and hat, then Croft Indulgence is just the wine for you. Smooth, calm, cultured, utterly delicious, easy drinking and not remotely challenging, this wine is the antithesis of the Taylor's below, which will flay your taste buds and reassemble your innards in true port style.

£9.99 **Taylor's Late Bottled Vintage Port, 2000**, Douro Valley, Portugal (**Asd**, **Boo**, **Maj**, **Mor**, **Odd**, **Sai**, **Tes**, **Thr**, **Unw** and **Wai**). I am happy to say that Taylor's LBV 2000 is spectacular. It has the structure of 1996, the nose of 1997, brawn of 1998, the flesh of 1999 and the flamboyance associated with the millennium year. In short, this is the definitive bottle of port, and it is sold everywhere at a tenner, offering the most extraordinary value for money.

£13.95 **Banyuls Cuvée Réserva, Domaine de la Tour Vieille, NV**, Roussillon, France (**Yapp**). Tasting like a fruitier version of a tawny port, this is sensational. Chill it down a touch and the raisiny, plum and walnut flavours are simply hypnotic in the glass. This is a full bottle and it would last a week once opened, so there is no hurry to drink this nectar. My dream date for Cuvée Réserva would be a gooey ginger tart – or Geri Halliwell.

£14.99 50cl bottle, **Campbells Classic Rutherglen Liqueur Muscat, NV**, Rutherglen, Victoria, Australia (**Bacchanalia**, **D Byrne**, **Cooden**, **Nidderdale** and **Winesmith**). This is a spectacular wine that will reward every one of your senses with a cornucopia of brazen flavours – hazelnut, raisin, singed plums, old fashioned toffee, rose petals, crème brûlée and many, many more. Make a list – you'll need a piece of A3!

£15.25 **Quinta de la Rosa LBV, Port, 1998,** Douro Valley, Portugal (**Bedales**, **Butlers**, **Constantine**, **Dunells** and **Sommelier**). I have always loved the wines and ports from this fantastic estate, and this mighty 1998 is no exception. Fully ripe and dark, with brooding power but a very juicy finish, this is the sort of wine that will impress the connoisseur and novice alike.

£24.99 **Taylor's Quinta de Vargellas, 1996**, Port, Portugal (**Fortnum & Mason**, **Harrods**, **Maj**, **Odd**, **Sai**, **Selfridges** and **Tes**). With some of the oldest vines in the Douro, Quinta de Vargellas is a heroic brew. With ten years under its belt and a flavour that conjures up gentleman's clubs and Gussie Finknottle, this is just the wine for late nights in when it is blowing a gale outside and you have a roaring fire in the hearth. Feet up, large schooners please.

A–Z OF FOOD
AND WINE
COMBINATIONS

INTRODUCTION

What delights me more than anything about this book is that this chapter is pored over as much as the Top 250. I know this because everywhere I go, on book signings and wine-tasting events, people tell me that the following seventy or so pages have helped to guide them towards getting dinner parties 'right' and impressing their own palates along the way, as well as those of their guests. It isn't rocket science, though; rather a case of telling the truth about what works and what doesn't in the flavour-combination arena. You will find that you swiftly learn the basic rules of food-and-wine matching and how these combos impact on your palate. You probably have most of them cracked already. I say this because you match food ingredients all of the time without even thinking. When making a sandwich it is generally accepted that ham goes well with mustard and beef with horseradish, but not necessarily the other way around. I know the flavour of most of the wines out there on the shelves because I spend every moment of every day tasting, and you know what your palate likes. Put two and two together and food-and-wine matching is about getting ham and mustard on the same page while avoiding the ham and horseradish!

I realise that everything is a matter of taste – this is a subjective subject if ever there was one. So, if you are new to this book, it is important that you realise I don't tell you exactly what to drink with your dinner (that would, by definition, only work for my own palate), but I tell you what not to drink, as much as gently guide you to a flavour or collection of wines that would work well. It is up to you where to make your final decision, by plumping for a bottle that you know you like.

You can therefore relax (and open a bottle – I would!). It need no longer be a nightmare trying to match wine to food when you are out and about or entertaining at home. Forget the pressure to 'get it right'.

When I am not writing wine articles or books, I work as a wine consultant to restaurants around the world. My job involves writing wine lists and teaching waiting staff about wine. This invaluable experience, over nearly twenty years, has helped me to compile this chapter. There is nothing more exciting than setting up a wine list for a new restaurant. Talking to the chef and manager, tasting the dishes, anticipating the clientele, seeing the size of the cellar or storage area, and formulating a budget, all help me towards my decisions. What is rather bizarre is that the same thought processes happen when you are cooking dinner for friends – albeit on a smaller scale. Perhaps this is why I feel so comfortable writing this chapter and recommending wine styles to you.

Your first step is to think of a menu, then find the dish in the A–Z and read through my recommendations. Now you have a choice. Either riffle through this year's Top 250 and find the exact bottle you need – just hunt by style and price and you'll be there in a trice. Quick, easy and you'll be drinking one of the best wines in the world. Alternatively, peruse the Gazetteer section and make a shopping list of several producers in the category of wines you need, then flick through the Merchants pages and phone around. Or, if you are feeling brave, just head out of your front door, book in hand, and wing it. This is the way to gain confidence and, if you play your cards right, you could well find a real surprise on the shelves. Whatever you decide, I wish you the best of luck and happy drinking.

One small tip – grab a few bottles of a multi-purpose, multi-talented style of wine while you're at it. Some names pop up in this chapter more often than others – Sauvignon Blanc, the crowd-pleasing, refreshing, dry, white grape is always a winner and definitely a safe place to go if you are worried. As are the juicy, smooth, black-fruit-driven, New World GSM (Grenache, Shiraz, Mourvèdre) blends – try to keep a few bottles of these styles of wine at home in readiness for unexpected guests or impromptu cooking. It is also worth pointing out that Beaujolais, once one of the most ridiculed styles of wine in France, is incredibly versatile in the kitchen. It appears over twenty-five times in this chapter and it is a style of wine you mustn't miss!

I met up with some old pals the other day at a neutral venue (i.e. not one of the restaurants whose wine lists I know well) for a lunch party. I bet you know what is coming! Everyone wanted to order different things and the wine list was opened in front of yours truly. I quickly conducted a straw poll of starters and main courses. I thought that by ordering one bottle of red and one bottle of white, I could at least have a chance to chat and give myself a breather before having to order another bottle. Following my own rules, I chose a fresh, zingy New Zealand Sauvignon Blanc and a stunning bottle of Chiroubles (Beaujolais). Every base was covered, from oysters, spring rolls, pâté, calamari and Caesar salad for starters, to steak sandwich, soss and mash, seared tuna, lasagne and roast lamb for the main course. In the end, we just ordered the same bottles again because they were such a hit! The Sauvignon effortlessly sliced through the oysters, the fish dishes, the Caesar and the chilli sauce in the dip for the calamari. The Beaujolais wasn't too heavy for the pâté, but had enough character and fruit weight to cope with the meaty main courses. It is for this reason that these wines are so incredibly popular in the first place. There isn't a bar in Paris that doesn't sell Beaujolais and Sauvignon Blanc by the gallon (although I am pretty sure that they would get their Sauvignon from the Loire Valley as opposed to New Zealand!).

APÉRITIF WINE STYLES

Pre-dinner nibbles like *dry roasted almonds*, *bruschetta*, *cashews*, *canapés*, *crostini*, *crudités*, *olives* and *gougères* (those heavenly cheese puffs served by the plateful in Burgundy and Chablis) are designed to give your palate a jump-start and get your juices flowing before a feast. It is important at this stage of the proceedings not to overload your taste buds with big, weighty, powerful wines. Save those bottles for later and zero in on refreshing, taste-bud-awakening styles that set the scene, rather than hog the limelight: Champagne is, not surprisingly, the perfect wine if you're feeling loaded but, if not, sparkling wines from the Loire (Saumur), the south of France (Limoux) or Crémant de Bourgogne (Burgundy) would do the job nicely. Italy offers up superb, dry, palate-enlivening fizz in the form of Prosecco from Veneto, or some more serious sparklers from Franciacorta, Trentino or Alto Adige. I never really drink the Spanish fizz Cava unless I'm in Barcelona because there are only a few worthy versions to be found in the UK. The best, authentic, Champagne-taste-alikes come from the New World. These are usually very good value, too (around half the price of Champs) – New Zealand, Australia (particularly Tasmania) and California are the places to go to find awesome quality.

Fino- and manzanilla-style sherries are wonderful palate cleansers, particularly with salty dishes, despite being thought of as perpetually 'out of fashion'. The least expensive option (and often safest, particularly if you are eating out) is a zesty, uplifting, palate-sprucing dry white. Even a moderately expensive number is often half the price of a bottle of Champs and there are thousands of these around, so go for it. There are also loads of first-class examples in this book. Stay with unoaked styles and keep the price under control, and then step up the pace with the next

bottle when the food hits the table. If the choice is poor
(a short restaurant wine list or a poorly stocked off licence)
then grab a neutral, dry, inexpensive white wine (Loire?)
and pep it up with a dash of Crème de Cassis (blackcurrant
liqueur) to make a Kir. Use the same liqueur to turn a dry,
sparkling wine or inexpensive Champagne into a glitzy
Kir Royale.

STARTERS AND MAIN COURSES
Anchovies Strongly flavoured whether they are fresh or
cured, these little hairy fish (whether you like 'em or not)
require dry, unoaked, tangy, acidic whites or juicy, bone-dry
rosés for maximum impact. Head to Italy, Spain or France
and keep the budget low – a fiver is all you need. There are a
few worthy rosés from the New World, but watch the
alcohol level, as they can stray a little high up the scale (stay
under 14% vol for safety). Dry sherry is also spot on, but
consider what is in the rest of the dish, as it can be quite a
strong flavour.

Antipasti The classic Italian mixed platter of *artichokes,
prosciutto, bruschetta, olives, marinated peppers* and
aubergines enjoys being romanced with chilled, light Italian
reds like Valpolicella and Bardolino, or clean, vibrant,
refreshing whites like Pinot Grigio, Pinot Bianco, Frascati,
Falanghina, Vernaccia, Greco, Est! Est!! Est!!!, Orvieto,
Verdicchio or Gavi.

Artichokes Dry, unoaked, refreshing whites are best here,
especially if you are going to dip the artichokes in *vinaigrette*
(see 'Vinaigrette'). Alsatian Sylvaner, Pinot Blanc, lighter
Riesling, Loire Sauvignon Blanc or Aligoté from Burgundy
are perfect partners from France, as are the Italian whites
listed above for 'Antipasti'. If you want to head to the New

World, then keep it angular and edgy with South African or New Zealand Sauvignon Blanc, or Argentinean Torrontés.

Asparagus Because of its inbuilt asparagusy characteristics (see my tasting note on page 176), Sauvignon Blanc is the perfect match here. New World styles of Sauvignon from Chile (Casablanca), Australia (Adelaide Hills) or New Zealand (Marlborough) have tons of flavour and would be better suited to asparagus dishes that have *hollandaise*, *balsamic vinegar* or *olive oil* and *Parmesan*. Old World styles, like those from the Loire (Sancerre, Menetou-Salon and Pouilly-Fumé) are great if the dish is plainer. Northern Italian whites like Pinot Bianco or Pinot Grigio, as well as South African Sauvignon Blanc (somewhere between New Zealand and Loire geographically and in style) would also do the job.

Aubergines If served grilled with *pesto* or *olive oil*, *garlic* and *basil*, as always you must identify the most dominant flavours in the dish. In both of these recipes they are the same – garlic and basil – so tackle them with a dry Sauvignon Blanc or keen, white Italians like Verdicchio, Inzolia, Fiano or Falanghina. Plain aubergine dishes are fairly thin on the ground as these glossy, sleek, black beauties are often used within vegetarian recipes (for example, *ratatouille* or *caponata*). If cheese or meat (*moussaka*) is involved, these flavours take over, so light, youthful reds are required. Southern Italian or Sicilian Primitivo, Nero d'Avola or Aglianico, southern French Grenache-based blends, Chilean Carmenère, Spanish Garnacha or Aussie Durif are all good matches (and great value, too). Just make sure they are not too ponderous or alcohol heavy. If the dish is hotter (spicier), or the aubergines are *stuffed*, you will need a more feisty, characterful red. But don't be tempted by anything too heady (avoid tannic red grapes like Cabernet, Pinotage,

Nebbiolo, Zinfandel and Malbec). *Imam bayildi*, the classic aubergine, onion, olive oil and tomato dish, is a winner with juicy, slightly chilled Chilean Merlot, youthful, bright purple Valpolicella, spicy Sardinian Cannonau or black-fruit-imbued Italians – Barbera d'Alba, Carmignano, Montepulciano d'Abruzzo or Morellino di Scansano.

Australian The masters/inventors of Asian fusion Down Under manage to juggle the freshest of land and sea ingredients, and weave into them the best of Asia's spices and presentation. This beguiling and thoroughly delicious style of cuisine is a real hit worldwide, as the cooking is virtually fat free and its packed with zesty, palate-enlivening flavours. It is no surprise that in trendy Sydney, Adelaide, Perth and Melbourne restaurants they reward their palates with finely tuned Clare and Eden Valley Rieslings, fresh, grapey Verdelhos, zippy, perky Adelaide Hills and Western Australian Sauvignon Blancs and assorted Pinot Gris, Semillon/Sauvignon blends and keen, fresh, oak-balanced Chardonnays. Not all Aussie reds are huge and porty, with the vogue for more aromatic wines coming from McLaren Vale, Great Western or Frankland (Shiraz), Tasmania, Mornington, Geelong or Yarra (Pinot Noir), and cooler Margaret River or Orange (Cabernet/Merlot) really hitting form. It is no wonder they are so fit and healthy down there with such glorious local produce, awesome wines and inspired chefs!

Avocado If the avocado is *undressed*, you need light, unoaked whites, in particular Loire Sauvignon Blanc, Muscadet or fresh, cheap, clean Italians. If *dressed* with *vinaigrette* or with *Marie Rose sauce* (in a prawn cocktail), richer Sauvignon Blanc (NZ and the Cape), Pinot Gris (smart Italians and New Zealand) or Australian Verdelho and Riesling are spot on, as are young, white Rhônes and Alsatian Pinot

Blanc. *Guacamole*, depending on its chilli heat, needs cool, citrusy, dry whites to douse the palate and cut through the gloopy green mush.

Bacon This usually pops up as an ingredient in a dish and not often as the main theme (unless you've had a heavy night on the sherbets and need the finest of all miracle cures – a *bacon sarnie*!). If you feel like a glass of wine to accompany this classic bread and hog delight or your *full English breakfast* (I know I do), then chilled red Côtes-du-Rhône, Languedoc Rouge or Cru Beaujolais would be a joy. If you are brave (or foolish, or both) try it with a sparkling Shiraz from Down Under. If you are using fried or grilled *pancetta* or *lardons* in a salad, remember that the salty flavour and/or smoked taste could prompt a move away from a salady, light white wine to a juicy, fresh red. Red Burgundy (a smart Bourgogne Rouge is as far as you need go) is heavenly with *bacon and eggs* – even if a little ostentatious.

Barbecues The unplanned, off-the-cuff, ever-so-slightly flammable nature of the British barbecue, combined with unlimited platters groaning with pink, uncooked meat, spicy, lurid marinades and intense, mahogany-coloured, smoky sauces, ensures an informal and always flavour-packed occasion. Aim for good value New World gluggers (white or red), so long as they are assertive, juicy and fruit-driven. Lightly oaked Chardonnay, Chenin Blanc or Semillon for whites, or inexpensive Zinfandel, Merlot, Carmenère, Cabernet Sauvignon or Shiraz for reds all work. Don't be afraid of chilling both the whites and reds for maximum effect. Chile, Argentina, Australia, South Africa and New Zealand are the most likely candidates for your guest list.

Beans With *baked beans* you simply need to find fruity, berry-driven reds because the tomato sauce flavour is so dominant and it takes over the palate. Any youthful reds with refreshing acidity, such as those from the Loire, Spain, South Africa, South America or Italy, will work well. Remember to keep the price down – it's not worth spending over a tenner for a *beans-on-toast* wine, unless you are a little loopy or feeling flush! Not surprisingly, anything goes with *green beans*, as they are the least flavourful of veggies. You'd have to mince along with a light, dry white to let a green bean truly express itself! *Tuscan bean salad* needs slightly chilled, light-bodied reds or fresh, zingy whites to cut through the earthy flavours. If you throw some beans into a stew, in a *cassoulet* or any of a wide variety of Spanish dishes, then Grenache/Carignan blends from the south of France (Fitou, Corbières, Faugères or Minervois), or Garnacha-based wines from Spain (Navarra, Terra Alta, Priorato, Campo de Borja, Calatayud or Tarragona) will easily deal with the beanie ballast. *Black bean sauce* requires a few moments' meditation and trepidation. The curious, oil-slick texture and intensity of dark sweetness must be countered by huge, juicy, mouth-filling, velvety smooth reds – Zinfandel is the only red grape brave enough to cope. *Refried beans*, either in *tacos* or other *Mexican* dishes, have a fair degree of earthy sludginess that needs either rich whites like a bright New World Chardonnay (Chile, South Africa and Australia give the best value) or fresh, fruity reds. I would try Bonarda, Sangiovese or Tempranillo from Argentina as a starting point, then head over to Chile for some Carmenère or Merlot if you have no joy. My favourite bean is the noble *cannellini*, the base for all great bean-frenzy soups. What should you uncork? Unlucky – you'll have to wait with spoon and glass at the ready for the 'Soup' entry

Beef As there are so many different beef dishes, it is lucky the rules are not too tricky. Reds, predictably, are the order of the day. But it is the size and shape of them (the wines, not the cows) that determine just how accurate the match will be. *Roast beef* (or *en croûte/beef Wellington*) served up for Sunday lunch deserves a modicum of respect. When you gather around the dining room table do, by all means, push the boat out.

It is at times like these when old-fashioned, gentleman's red Bordeaux really comes into its own. Don't ask me why, but classy wines such as red Bordeaux, Bandol, erudite northern Rhônes – Hermitage, Crozes-Hermitage, Cornas, St-Joseph or Côte-Rôtie – or even Italy's answer to an Aston Martin V12 Vanquish, the Super-Tuscans (see the stellar list in the Gazetteer) are simply magnificent with this king of beef dishes. As you'd expect, not one of these wines is remotely affordable (nor is the car, mind you!). They are all special-occasion wines, so if you are looking to shave a few pounds off your credit card bill, I would recommend heading to the top Cabernets from Australia's Margaret River (Western Australia) or Coonawarra (South Australia), or Napa Valley in California. You've guessed it, these are again fairly dear, but at least these reds will give you the richness and complexity that you are craving. If you are on a strict budget, then don't change regions, just buy cleverly – not all wines from Bordeaux are exorbitantly priced. Try the less famous sub-regions like Côtes de Castillon, Bourg, Blaye and Francs, and go for a good vintage (see my Vintage Table on page 240). These wines can really hit the spot. Hearty Southern Rhône or Languedoc reds would also do very well. Most Aussie (try Clare Valley and McLaren Vale in particular), South African, Chilean and Argentinean Cabernets or Cab/Shiraz blends around the tenner mark offer charm, complexity and competence, especially if you stick to my recommendations. It is at this price point that the New World leads the pack. But even if you drop down to around a fiver you can still have fun, just remember to stick to hotter-climate wines, as red Bordeaux and red Rhônes at this price can be pretty dire.

One question you must ask yourself is, 'How do you like your beef cooked?' If you are a keen carnivore and a fan of *rare* beef, you can safely drink younger, more tannic red wines, as the harder tannins balance perfectly with juicy, rare meat, slicing through the flesh and making your mouth water. If, however, you like your beef *well done*, then choose an older wine with smoother, more harmonious tannins.

Stews, *casseroles* and *meat pies* need richer, more structured reds, particularly if meaty, stock-rich gravy is involved. Cabernet Sauvignon, Syrah (Shiraz), Pinotage, Piemontese (northern Italian) reds, Zinfandel and Malbec are but a few of the superb, hunky, robust grapes to go for. Look for wines from South Africa, Australia, California and Argentina. Southern Rhônes like Gigondas, Lirac, Cairanne, Rasteau or Vacqueyras will also be superb, as will Provençal or Languedoc reds made from a similar blend of swarthy red grapes. Portuguese wines are worth considering with rich beef dishes – the red wines from Dão and the Douro Valley are still woefully under-priced and, if you peruse my Gazetteer recommendations, mightily impressive. Cahors in southwest France also deserves a mention, as it is a skilful beef partner. *Bollito misto*, the Italian stew made from beef and just about everything else you could find in your larder, demands the presence of local wines – Teroldego and Marzemino, from Trentino in northern Italy, would be a quirky and yet inspirational place to kick off, as would smart Valpolicella, Barbera and Dolcetto. *Boeuf bourguignon*, as the name suggests, usually pressgangs the help of red Burgundy. But please don't cook with anything expensive –

save your money for the drinking wine and cook with a simple generic bottle (Beaujolais or Bourgogne Rouge). *Steak and kidney pie* loves manly, rustic reds with grippy, palate-crunching acidity and sturdy tannins. These wines slice through the gravy and often-chewy kidneys – Madiran and Cahors from France, Malbec from Argentina, and New World war-horses, like South African Pinotage and Syrah and Aussie Shiraz also enjoy this challenge. *Cottage pie*, with carrot, celery, onions and minced beef rarely requires anything more challenging than an inexpensive, fun lovin' red. You could even try your hand with Eastern Europe (although don't expect me to road-test this for you), or southern Italy or Sicily (a safer bet), and then go crazy and buy two bottles. A heroic *Beef stroganoff* demands rusticity in its dancing partner, so gather together some southern Rhônes (Sablet, Valréas, Cairanne or Vacqueyras); even a straight Côtes-du-Rhône from the right domaine can be a joy (see the Gazetteer page 173). *Hungarian goulash* would be wonderfully authentic if a Hungarian red wine joined it. Nuff said! But if you want to play a straighter bat, head to Rioja, Navarra, La Mancha or Toro (Spain) or Chilean Cabernet Sauvignon.

Straight *steak* has a more direct and controlled meaty flavour than a rich stew, so finer wines can be dragged out of the cellar (or local merchant). Bathe in Chianti, Brunello di Montalcino, Ribera del Duero, Californian Merlot, Zin or Cab, top-end Cru Beaujolais (still only a tenner!), Crozes-Hermitage, St-Joseph (both Rhônes), and South African, Argentinean, cool-climate Australian and New Zealand Cabernet Sauvignon or Shiraz. Watch out that you don't OD on *Béarnaise sauce* that, though great with a mouthful of steak, can clog up the taste buds (and the waist band). With *steak au poivre*, the pungent, pulverised peppercorns make their presence known in each and every mouthful, so look for meaty (and pepper-flavoured) wines like northern Rhône reds (Syrah) or their cousins from further afield – Shiraz from Australia, Chile or South Africa. *Burgers* (homemade, of course, not mechanically reclaimed at the golden arches!) – heaven in a bun – often served with ketchup, bacon, cheese or relish (or all of the above), crave fruity reds like Italian Dolcetto or Barbera, Spanish Garnacha, young Rioja Crianza, juicy Californian Zinfandel, South African Pinotage, Chilean or South African Merlot, and Australian Petit Verdot (hard to find, but dead funky) or Shiraz blends. Once again, go for younger wines if you like your burger rare, and older, more mellow wines if you dwell at the well-done end of the spectrum. *Chilli con carne* is a difficult dish to match with wine. As with burgers, it is necessary to search for fruitier styles like Aussie Merlot, or Negroamaro and Nero d'Avola from southern Italy and Sicily – I quite like chilling them a touch, too. *Steak tartare* is a strange one, as I'm still not sure whether I actually really like it (a side issue), but I must admit it works terrifically well with very light reds and rosés – Tavel (southern Rhône) and other Grenache-based rosés (try Spain or Australia) are perfect, as are snooty Pinot Noirs like Sancerre red or rosé. If you fancy splashing out, then rosé Champagne is the ultimate combo (although people are bound to think you're a show off). Whatever you do, make sure you go easy on the capers if they are served alongside – they are mini hand grenades on the palate, spoiling a seamless vinous performance.

Cold, rare roast beef salad and other cold-beef dishes enjoy the company of fresh, light reds with low tannins – Beaujolais, Valpolicella, red Loires (either Cabernet Franc or Gamay) or Argentinean Tempranillo or Bonarda would all work. Pinot Noir is also a treat with this style of dish – Burgundy, Martinborough, Marlborough or Central Otago (all NZ), Tasmania, Yarra Valley and Mornington (all Oz). The only occasion when you are allowed to break the red-wine-with-beef rule (of course there has to be one) is with *carpaccio* (raw/rare) or *bresaola* (air-dried). These wafer-thin-sliced beef dishes can handle whites. Any dry, apéritif-style Italian white or light Montepulciano-style red would be fantastico.

Cajun see 'Mexican'.

Capers Sauvignon Blanc, from almost anywhere, or very dry Italian whites like Soave (Veneto) or Greco, Fiano or Falanghina (Campania) are very good matches, as they can cut through the peculiar, green, otherworldly, vinegary tanginess you experience when you crunch and burst open the exoskeleton of an unsuspecting caper. (For more suggestions see 'Apéritif'.)

Caviar I know it is a sin, but I adore decent caviar. Sevruga or Oscietra (not Beluga – ridiculously decadent and a little too 'fishy' for my taste) are my faves and Champagne is definitely the call of the day. Avoid rosé styles, though (they always tend to taste metallic with caviar, in my experience), and there is no need to pop the cork of a prestige cuvée unless you're desperately trying to impress (or are a tasteless lottery winner – congrats, by the way). If you want to keep the budget down, and there is nothing wrong with that, then Sancerre, Pouilly-Fumé (Loire) or tighter, leaner South African and New Zealand Sauvignons are all stunning combos. These styles also work if caviar is used in a sauce, but do look to the main ingredient as well as the caviar for guidance.

Charcuterie A selection of charcuterie (*assiette de charcuterie* to be precise, including *saucisson*, *salami*, *ham* etc.) contains loads of diverse flavours along a similar textural theme. I love smart rosés (I am not afraid to admit it) and top-quality, slightly chilled Beaujolais or Gamay from the Loire. Light to medium Italian reds, like Freisa (Piemonte), Valpolicella (Veneto), Morellino di Scansano (Tuscany), Montepulciano d'Abruzzo (Marche) or Aglianico (from the south) would also be good matches (take a few degrees off these, too, in the fridge). If you favour whites, then stick to firm, rich white grape varieties like Riesling or Pinot Gris, which usually manage to harness at least as much flavour intensity as the reds anyway. Do watch out for pickles, gherkins, cornichons (wicked little French numbers) or caperberries, as excess vinegar will guarantee that you'll not be able to taste the next mouthful of wine! My advice is to shake your gherkin first (ooh, err, Missus), endeavouring to knock off as much vinegar as possible before squirrelling them away. (For *chorizo* and *spicy salami*, see 'Pork'.)

Cheese (cooked) There is a groaning cheese-board section at the end of this hedonistic chapter, so flick on for uncooked cheese joy. *Cauliflower cheese* (*leek Mornays*, *cheesy pasta* dishes etc.) and straight *cheese sauces*, depending on the strength of cheese used, need medium- to full-bodied whites such as New World Chardonnay, Chenin Blanc and Semillon. For reds, you must join the quest for fresh acidity coupled with pure berry fruit. This hunt should lead you to the delicious wines from the Loire (Saumur-Champigny, Chinon or Bourgueil) or Chilean, Australian or South African Merlot, Italian Cabernet Franc, Lagrein, Dolcetto or Freisa, or youthful Rioja, Navarra, Somontano or Campo de Borja reds from Spain.

Fondue needs bone-dry whites (or pints of bloody good lager!) to cut through the waxy, stringy, molten cheese. If you are a perfectionist then you'd be trekking off, crampons and silly hat ahoy, in search of the inoffensive, and frankly frighteningly dull, wines from Savoie – Chignin-Bergeron,

Abymes, Crépy or Apremont. However, if you are keen on rewarding your palate with pleasant-tasting, accurate wines, then well-balanced, fully ripe (as opposed to upsettingly lean and enamel-challengingly acidic) styles like Alsatian Pinot Blanc, Riesling and Sylvaner, and fresh Loire Sauvignon Blanc or Chenin Blanc would be ideal. You could even try dry Portuguese whites and various northeastern Italian single varietals like Pinot Gris or Pinot Blanc. *Raclette* would love to be partnered with light red Burgundies or juicy Beaujolais-Villages.

With *cheese soufflé* (one of the true gems in the cooked cheese repertoire) you can really go out on a limb. Argentinean Torrontés, or any aromatic dry whites like Muscat (Alsace), Riesling (from Alsace or Clare Valley/Eden Valley/Frankland in Australia) or even lighter Gewürztraminer (Tasmania or Alto Adige in Italy are worth a punt) would all be delicious. If the soufflé has any other hidden ingredients inside remember to consider them before plumping for a bottle – with *smoked haddock soufflé* you'd be wise to follow the fish so opt for punchy, lemony whites, like Semillon or Riesling.

Mozzarella, with its unusual milky flavour and play-doh texture, is well suited to Italian Pinot Bianco, Pinot Grigio, good Vernaccia, Arneis, Gavi and Verdicchio. Yes, these are all Italians! *Grilled goats' cheese* is equally at home with Sancerre (remember the best goats' cheese hails from Chavignol, Sancerre's finest village) and Pouilly-Fumé (across the other side of the Loire river) and all other Sauvignon Blancs from around the world (South Africa would be my first choice if your Loire fridge is empty). Lighter reds also work, particularly if you are tucking into a salad with some ham joining in the fun. Goats' cheese is pretty forgiving when it comes down to it, but avoid oaked whites and tannic or heavy reds.

Chicken Chicken is very accommodating – it loves both whites and reds. But be careful because it is a touch fussy when it comes to the precise grape varieties you want to set it up with. Chardonnay is chicken's favourite white grape by far, with Riesling coming in a close second. Pinot Noir is the bird's favourite red (it's every bird's favourite red – be honest!), with Gamay, perhaps surprisingly, claiming the runner-up spot. This means that a well-educated, classy chicken loves every village in my beloved Burgundy region, and who can blame it?

Lighter dishes such as *cold chicken* are fairly versatile, so look to my *al fresco*-style wines in the 'Picnics' section. *Cold chicken and ham pie* works well with lighter, fragrant reds and deeper-coloured, sturdy rosés from the southern Rhône, Beaujolais and Australia. If you are feeling adventurous, then try chilling down a bottle of Beaujolais-Villages to white temperature – it's a super, if unusual, match. *Poached chicken* can handle the same sort of wines but with a little more flesh – both Old and New World Pinot Noir work here. White wine companions include lighter New World Chardonnay or French Country Viognier and Marsanne/Roussanne blends. Possibly my favourite dish of all time, *roast chicken*, follows this theme once again, but takes it a stage further. Finer (by that I mean more expensive) red and white Burgundy, elegant, cooler climate New Zealand or Australian or Californian Chardonnay and Pinot Noir, and top flight Beaujolais (again) are all wonderful matches. *Coq au vin* also works well with red Burgundy, but you can scale the wine down to a Chalonnaise version, a Hautes-Côtes or Bourgogne rouge (from one of my reputable producers, of course). *Chicken casserole* or *pot pie* ups the ante even further and it enjoys a broader wine brief. Medium-weight Rhône reds and New World Grenache-based wines, as well as mildly oaky

Chardonnays, are all in with a shout. *Chicken and mushroom pie*, *fricassee* and other chicken dishes with *creamy sauces* call out to Chardonnay and beyond – dry Riesling from Germany, Alsace (France), or Clare Valley, Eden Valley, Frankland or Tasmania (Australia), Alsatian Tokay-Pinot Gris and funky Rhône whites. New World Pinot Noir (from California, New Zealand, Tassie or Victoria in Oz) is the only red variety to feel truly at home here.

OK, so far things have been fairly straightforward, but I am now going to throw a few obstacles in front of our feathered friend, as *chicken Kiev* changes the rules completely. Full, rich and even part-oak-aged Sauvignon Blanc or Sauvignon/ Semillon blends are needed to take on the buttery/garlic onslaught – white Graves (Bordeaux) and California does this well with their Fumé Blancs, as does Margaret River in Western Australia, but watch this space as this style is starting to be made all over the world. Not content with this hurdle, *coronation chicken*, depending on who is making it (I like a lot of spicy naughtiness in my sauce), can also have a bit of a kick, so dry Riesling from New Zealand or Clare Valley/Eden Valley in Australia would be worth unscrewing. Lastly, *barbecued chicken wings* can be nuclear-hot (Si Jukesy is a veritable Tardis when slotting these) and, in my experience, beer is usually the best bet. If, for some reason, you would like open a bottle of wine (are you mad?), then a clean, inexpensive New World Chardonnay will work.

Chilli *Enchiladas, chimichangas* (nuclear waste in a wrap), *fajitas, chilli con carne, dragon's breath pizzas* (just ask Shrek) and any other fart-lightingly hot Mexican dishes 'embrace the dark side' with a hefty dose of chillies. Thirst-quenching, chillable Italian red grape varieties like Primitivo, Nero d'Avola, Frappato or Negroamaro, or juicy New World

Bonarda, Durif, Cab Sauv and Merlot are needed to cool you down and rebuild your taste buds. If you need a bottle of white, then New World Chardonnay or Semillon, thoroughly chilled, will have enough texture and body to handle the heat. I love Clare Valley Riesling with chilli-laden seafood or chicken dishes, but keep the price sub-tenner. Good Luck and May the Force be with You!

Chinese The perennial problem when matching wine to Chinese food is that, the second you and your pals see the menu, everyone wants something different and, of course, everyone is an expert! So, in the end, you settle on sharing your dishes with your mates and find yourself tasting every dish on the table, thus mixing flavours wildly. Sweet-and-sour dishes slam into spicy ones, stir-fried dishes envelop crispy chilli ones, while poor old plain-boiled food struggles for a break in the non-stop, kick-boxing palate action. John Woo would be proud of the mayhem, but your taste buds are crying for a break, so this means Chinese-friendly wines must be multi-skilled, pure, fruit-driven offerings with lashings of all-important, crisp acidity. Tannic, youthful reds and oaky, full-bodied whites are completely out of bounds – the thugs. White grape varieties to consider (in unoaked form) are Sauvignon Blanc, Riesling, Semillon, Pinot Gris, Greco (southern Italy), Verdelho (totally underrated from Australia) and bone-dry Gewürztraminer. Reds are a little more difficult, as there are only a few truly juicy varieties, but New World Merlot, Argentinean Bonarda and cheaper Californian Zinfandels are all good bets. It is no surprise that Antipodean wines work well with this style of cooking as Asia is on their doorstep. Hao chi, Ganbei.

Chutney see 'Pâté' and 'Pork'.

Duck *Roast* or *pan-fried* duck is often served with fruit or fruity sauces, so you need to be prepared to balance this with a fruity wine. Reds are de rigueur here – New World Pinot Noir (loads to choose from), good quality Beaujolais, Italian Barbera or Negroamaro, Australian Chambourcin (OK, this is rare, but what a challenge!), lighter Californian Zinfandel and any other super-juicy, berry-drenched wines would do the business. *À l'orange* swings the colour firmly to white, but full-flavoured, juicy wines are still the vogue. Alsace or top Aussie Riesling, Alsatian Tokay-Pinot Gris, or Southern French and Rhône Viognier all have enough richness and texture to crack this dish, as do top-end northern Italian white blends – see Alto Adige and Friuli in the Gazetteer for the best estates. With *cherries*, 'village-level' red Burgundy (utilising the beautifully cherry-scented red grape Pinot Noir), top notch Barbera from Piedmont, smart, new wave Reserva-level Rioja and medium-weight but classy Zins from California are all excellent. The more robust dish of *confit de canard* demands meatier reds with backbone, grippy acidity and tannin to cut through the sauce and fat that makes this dish sing, like those from Bandol in Provence, the Languedoc-Roussillon or the southwest of France – Madiran or Cahors for example. For an unlikely but first-class combo, give *crispy aromatic duck* a whirl with chilled Chambourcin or Durif from Australia, or juicy, fruit-driven Californian Zinfandel (you need only spend £6 or £7) – they are a dead cert.

Eggs For *quiches*, *soufflés* or *light*, *savoury tarts* consider the main flavours (ham, cheese, herbs etc.) and their impact on the dish. Also, think about what you are eating with it – these dishes are always served with something else. Once you have nailed these flavours, unoaked or lightly oaked Chardonnay is a fair starting point – Chablis is a classic, but northeastern Italian Chardonnays would also be spot on. New World unoaked (just say no to oak) Chardonnays are now creeping through, too. *Omelettes*, *frittata* and *savoury pancakes* follow the same rules. However, for *oeufs en meurette* (the legendary Burgundian dish of poached eggs in red wine with lardons – *à genoux*) a red wine is definitely called for – mid-priced Beaujolais or a fresh, young red Burgundy would be accurate. For *fried* and *poached* eggs, look at the other ingredients involved. If combined with a salad utilising stronger-flavoured ingredients, try Beaujolais but, if you'd rather go white, Alsatian Riesling or a top Pinot Blanc would be just fine. For *quails'* eggs, see the Apéritif wine styles. Finally, eggs *Benedict* has an awful lot going on, from the muffin base and bacon or ham, to the ridiculously wicked hollandaise sauce, so a youthful Côtes-du-Rhône is needed and would be a classic combination – you'll want a magnum.

Figs The only entry to feature in both this section and the pud category, figs are often served up, in season, when you are abroad on holiday. If you are anything like me then these are the most irresistible of fruit. Served with serious ham (in Italy) or in a salad, they manage to hold their own carnal flavours despite coming up against ingredients as combative as Gorgonzola and balsamic vinegar. Clearly those are the dominant flavours but if you really want to know what a fig likes to be drunk with there is only one answer – Riesling made with passion, knowing and all-encompassing sensitivity. Figs are, after all, the most erotic of ingredients and they must be rewarded with the most exotic and sensual of grape varieties.

Fish The flavour intensity of fish depends not only on the sort of fish you are cooking but also, crucially, on how it is cooked. The general rule is: the milder the flavour, the lighter the white wine; the richer the flavour, the heavier the white wine. I know this is obvious, but it is worth stating. Fish cooked in red wine is one of the few exceptions to this white-dominated section, as a light, fresh red would simply meld better with the sauce. From Bianco de Custoza and Soave (Italy), Austrian Grüner Veltliner, Menetou-Salon and Sauvignon de Touraine (Loire), white Burgundy (Mâcon, Rully, Pouilly-Fuissé, Meursault and so on), fine Californian Chardonnay, zesty Jurançon Sec, heady Australian or New Zealand Pinot Gris, plump Marsanne or whip-cracking Hunter Valley Semillon, to any aromatic Riesling or Viognier – the opportunities are literally endless. Just remember that poaching and steaming are gentler, non-taste-altering ways of cooking fish, while grilling, searing, frying and roasting all impart distinctive charred or caramelised nuances to the flesh. Also consider what you are cooking the fish with; check through your recipe for strongly flavoured ingredients, such as lemon, capers, balsamic vinegar, flavoured olive oil and pungent herbs. Often, the finer the piece of fish, the more money you should chuck at the wine.

Dover sole, lemon sole, turbot and sea bass, at the top of my Premier fish league, are all pretty pricey and, if you are that committed to a dish, you should endeavour to complete the picture by splashing out on a worthy bottle of white Burgundy. Failing that, for under a tenner you could pick up a top South African Chardonnay, Australian Semillon, Eden Valley or Clare Valley Riesling, Adelaide Hills Chardonnay, Riesling from Alsace, posh Lugana or Gavi from Italy, dry white Graves (Bordeaux), white Rhône or trendy Spanish Albariño to go with these fish. Halibut, John Dory, sea bream, skate and brill all enjoy these styles of wine, too, while swordfish, monkfish and hake can take on slightly weightier whites (or even a fresh, light red, such as Beaujolais). Salmon (poached or grilled) also likes Chardonnay, whether it is from the Old or New World, but give oaky styles a wide berth. *Trout* loves Riesling and the all-time classic Chablis. But, for an especially wicked combo, try to track down the unusually scented, dry French wine, Jurançon Sec. *Fish cakes*, especially proper ones with a high salmon content, go wonderfully with dry Riesling, richer Sauvignon Blancs or fresh Semillons, particularly if you are keen on a generous spoonful of tartare sauce (those grapes can handle it). *Red mullet* has more than enough character to cope with rosé wines, making a beautiful pink partnership between plate and glass.

Kedgeree is trickier (and if it's breakfast, slow down!), as the combo of smoked haddock, cayenne, parsley and egg might make you lean towards red. But don't! Rapier-like acidity is needed to slice through this dish and I'm sure you know which white grape does this best – Sauvignon Blanc. Sauvignon is also the grape to enjoy with *fish 'n' chips* (*cod*, *haddock* or *plaice*) because it can handle the batter (sometimes made with beer) and, to a certain degree, the vinegar (but go easy), and it shines with *fish pie* – poshest partnership being the Loire all-stars Pouilly-Fumé or Sancerre. If you fancy a trip to the New World, then Marlborough in New Zealand has to be the starting point for fans of this zesty grape, with South Africa being next and Australia's Margaret River giving the best Sem/Sauv blends outside Bordeaux.

Fish soups and *stews* need more weight in the glass, and one of the finest matches is white Rhône, made from Marsanne and Roussanne, or Viognier. Aussie Marsanne or Pinot Gris would also be a great option. *Sardines* require masses of perky acidity to cut through their oily flesh and, once again, Sauvignon Blanc is the winner. Having said this, don't forget poor old Muscadet or Italian Pinot Grigio, Arneis, Verdicchio or Gavi. Spanish Albariño, French

Aligoté and even light reds, like Gamay, would also be smashing. *Canned tuna* just needs unoaked, dry white wine – boring. However, *albacore*, the finer, paler version, is more delicately flavoured so take care not to swamp it. The Italian trio, Lugana, Bianco di Custoza and Soave Classico, would do this job inexpensively and with the required style. *Fresh tuna,* seared and served rare, desperately craves juicy, fresh, baby-light reds and chilled rosés (you could sneak a Sauvignon in, if you wish). *Brandade de morue* (salt cod), with its garlic and oil components, can stand up to whites with a little more soul. Albariño, from Galicia in Spain, is a perfect choice. However, Penedès whites and even light rosés are all within its grasp. *Herrings, kippers* and *rollmops* have a more robust texture and aroma thanks to the curing process. Once again, dry whites and rosés work well, but steer clear of oaked whites, as the pungent barrel nuances will overshadow the subtleties of the dish.

Smoked eel is often served with crème fraîche, and cream is always a little problematic for wine. Look to Austrian Riesling or Grüner Veltliner, top end Italian Pinot Grigio or bone-dry, world-class Riesling, and almost any dry white wine from Alsace. These will all relish the challenge. *Smoked salmon* is perfect with Gewürztraminer, whether it is from Alsace, Oz or Chile. Just make sure you buy a 'bone-dry', not 'off-dry' version. The scent and tropical nature of Gewürz may work amazingly well, but so does Viognier and even Canadian Pinot Blanc. Don't forget Champagne or top-end Tasmanian or Californian sparkling wine, particularly if serving blinis topped with smoked salmon and caviar. *Smoked trout* or *smoked mackerel pâté* is a challenge – fishy, smoky and creamy flavours all in one dish. Victorian Riesling, Hunter Valley Semillon, Adelaide Hills Sauvignon Blanc or Pinot Gris (all

Aussies), southern French Viognier, lighter Alsatian Riesling and Pinot Blanc are all perfect matches. Lastly, *curries* or *Asian* fish dishes often sport spices, such as turmeric, ginger and chilli, so turn to two of our favourite saviour white grapes for a solution – the New World Sauvignon Blanc's supreme confidence and Australia's world class, mind-blowing array of Rieslings – these are all stunning value. Yum.

Frogs' legs Leap for smooth, mildly oaked Chardonnay from Burgundy (Chablis, St-Romain, St-Aubin, Mâcon), Australia, South Africa or New Zealand. Consider what you've cooked these cheeky little blighters in and then tweak your wine choice accordingly – if *garlic butter* is involved, stick to Sauvignon Blanc. Good luck and keep the lid tight on the pan.

Game All flighted game, including *pheasant*, *quail*, *guinea fowl*, *woodcock*, *teal*, *grouse*, *snipe*, *wild duck* and *partridge* adore the majestic red grape Pinot Noir. This means red Burgundy is my first choice, with California, New Zealand, Tasmania, Victoria and Oregon somewhere in the pack behind the leader. The longer the bird is hung, the more mature the wine required (this can mean ten- or even twenty-year-old bottles). I have enjoyed red Bordeaux, Super-Tuscan, northern Rhône, Spanish wine from Ribera del Duero or Priorato, and many other top reds with this heady style of cuisine. But it is important to aim for complex wines with layers of fruit and a bit of age, and this inevitably means spending up.

Jugged hare often uses port and/or redcurrant jelly in the recipe, so a pretty feisty red wine is needed. New-style Piemontese reds made from Nebbiolo or Nebbiolo/Barbera blends would have the stuffing, as would more structured

Australian Shiraz (Clare, McLaren Vale, Heathcote or Barossa Valley), Zinfandel from California or South African Shiraz and Pinotage. One slightly cheaper and worthy source of full-bodied red is the Douro Valley in Portugal – not only would you have a meaty wine, but it would also be in perfect synergy if you've used port in the recipe. *Rabbit*, as well as being a less athletic version of hare, is also less pungent and has lighter-coloured flesh so, although big reds are essential, they don't need to be quite as powerful as those suggested for hare. The classic combo of *rabbit with mustard and bacon* packs a pungent flavour punch, so aim for swarthy bottles of red with feisty tannins and a youthful, purple hue – Chianti, Carmignano, Vino Nobile di Montepulciano (all from Tuscany), Bandol (from Provence), Lirac, Rasteau, Vacqueyras, Cairanne and Gigondas (from the southern Rhône), Argentinean Malbec, South African Cabernet and Shiraz, and smarter Chilean Cabernet blends would be spot on.

Wild boar favours rich, brooding reds and, depending on the dish, you could choose any of the aforementioned wines but, this time, add a few more of the finest of all Italian wines – Brunello di Montalcino, Barbaresco and Barolo. The only problem is you might need to win the lottery to buy a bottle. *Venison* loves reds and any bottle in this section would do, including top Australian Cabernet Sauvignon and some of the better New Zealand Hawke's Bay reds.

Finally, *game pie* – served cold it behaves like cold chicken and ham pie (see 'Chicken'), if served hot, open any wine suggested for steak and kidney pie (see 'Beef').

Garlic *Roast* garlic tends to emasculate fine wines so, if you are partial to lobbing a few bulbs in the oven, keep the wine spend down and follow the main dish's theme. *Garlic prawns*, *mushrooms* and *snails* all need aromatic, bone-dry, rapier-sharp Sauvignon Blanc. If you fancy being ahead of the pack and ever so patriotic, then try dry, herbal English white wines. Watch out for *Aïoli (garlic mayonnaise)* because you'll get a shock if your wine isn't up to it. Once again, Sauvignon Blanc can provide you with a shoulder to cry on, but you will have to find a bottle with a lot of character and vivacity – Marlborough in New Zealand is probably the answer. (For *chicken Kiev* see 'Chicken'.)

Goose The best wines for roast goose lie somewhere between those suited to game and those for chicken. In short, this means lighter red Burgundies and smooth, cherry-scented New World Pinot Noir in the red camp, and big, rich, sultry Chardonnays and Rieslings in the white. If you can afford it step up to Alsatian Grand Cru Riesling: you'll be in heaven.

Greek see 'Mezze'.

Haggis Traditionally accompanied by a wee dram of whisky but, if it could speak for itself (and some apparently do), a haggis would love to boogie with a rich, textured, aromatic white wine. Depending on your palate, you could choose a broad, luscious New World Chardonnay or a scented white Côtes-du-Rhône. If you really want to go over the top, try any Grand Cru Tokay-Pinot Gris from Alsace, or a Condrieu from the northern Rhône. If you want to save a few quid then look to the Eden Valley in South Australia for a funky, juicy Viognier.

Ham Smart Cru Beaujolais, Chilean Merlot or Carmenère, youthful Spanish Tempranillos, Italian Nero d'Avola, Montepulciano or Negroamaro, and youthful, inexpensive South African Merlot all have the essential juiciness to complement a glorious ham. The golden rule is to avoid any tannic or heavily acidic reds – stick to more mellow styles. There is a splinter group for whom heady whites also work – busty Viognier and lusty Chardonnay would do the task well. *Parma ham and melon, prosciutto, jamón Serrano* and *pata negra* all like dry German Riesling (Mosel, Rheingau or Pfalz), many of the aromatic whites from Trentino, Alto Adige and Friuli (northern Italy), and Verdejo or lightly oaked Viura from Rueda (Spain). *Honey-roast ham* needs mouth-filling, textural, bone-dry whites like dry Muscat, Viognier, Verdelho and Riesling. Search for these in Alsace, Australia, the Rhône Valley and from the vast array of terrific French Country wines (and grab some ripe figs to eat alongside it – so exotic and erotic!).

Ham hock with lentils or boiled Jersey potatoes and beetroot (or garden peas) is a treat with posh, dry rosé, and there are a fair few out there, so head to the southern Rhône or to richer examples of Sancerre rosé or Grenache rosés from McLaren Vale in Oz or Garnachas from Spain. *Smoked ham* has a fairly strong aroma and lingering flavour, so Tokay-Pinot Gris and young Vendange-Tardive-level Rieslings from Alsace would be exact, as would older Aussie Rieslings. If you favour red wine then choose a Merlot, a Cabernet Franc (from Australia or the Loire) or a Beaujolais, and chill it a degree or two to perk up its acidity. *Gammon steak* (sling the grim addition of pineapple or peaches) makes a neat partnership with oily, unoaked whites. All Alsatian wines and most dry German Rieslings would be delicious, as would the world-class Rieslings from Australia's Clare Valley, Eden Valley, Tasmania and Frankland. New Zealand Pinot Gris would also be fantastic. Semillon rarely gets the call up for a specific dish, but Aussie versions from the Hunter Valley and dry white Bordeaux (both with a smattering of oak) are simply stunning with ham, too.

Indian My Indian food-and-wine-matching career is taking off. In fact, it is now nothing short of a fully fledged passion. When I designed and wrote the wine list for the re-launch of top London Indian restaurant Chutney Mary, it was clear to me that unoaked or mildly oaked whites were to be the driving force in my selection. Smooth, juicy rosés were also essential, as were overtly fruit-driven reds, avoiding any that were noticeably tannic. The surprise came when I made the final selection and found that Italy, Australia, South Africa and New Zealand had claimed the lion's share of the list. There were a few wines from other countries but virtually no classics like red Bordeaux, Burgundy or Rhône. Shock horror! This just proves that, depending on the style of cuisine, a wine list can be balanced, eclectic and hopefully thoroughly exciting, without relying on France. The grape varieties or styles of wine that go particularly well with Indian food are: whites – Pinot Grigio, Verdicchio, Sauvignon Blanc, Pinot Bianco, Fiano, Torrontés, Riesling, Viognier, Verdelho, light Gewürztraminers and Albariño; reds – Valpolicella, Gamay (Beaujolais), Grenache (and Spanish Garnacha), Negroamaro, Pinot Noir, Nero d'Avola, Zinfandel, Barbera, Lagrein and Merlot. Other styles that work well include rich rosé, Prosecco, Asti (with puddings), rosé Champagne, Aussie sparklers and good-quality ruby port. Chutney Mary won Indian Restaurant of the Year at the Carlton Food Awards and then Amaya, a new sister restaurant, came along at the tail end of 2004 – wham bang. Best New Restaurant of the Year and also overall Restaurant of the Year in 2005 – you can see why I am having a good time!

Japanese *Sushi* is a strange, but utterly delicious, dish to match wine to. Surely green tea or sake (yuk) would be more appropriate? Well, I beg to differ – sparkling wines and Champagne are a treat with the best sushi, especially bone-dry cuvées – 'Ultra Brut', Zero Dosage or 'non dosage'. Not surprisingly, the ever-ready Sauvignon Blanc grape is waiting in the wings to save you and the bill. You could always look to zesty, unoaked Italian whites for joy – Vernaccia, Arneis and Gavi are all ideal. Perky Pinot Gris and Riesling from Australia and New Zealand would also be great. *Teriyaki* dishes are a nightmare to match wine to, though, as the sweetness and fruitiness in the glossy soy and sake glaze is incredibly flavour dominant on the palate. Zinfandel or rich Pinot Noir from California, super-ripe Chambourcin, lighter, modern Shiraz or Merlot from South Australia, and Nero d'Avola or Negroamaro from Sicily would just about manage this scary challenge – chill for effect. You will always be offered a blob of nuclear green matter with your sushi called wasabi. I'm afraid wasabi is a stealthy, committed, highly trained and silent wine assassin – thank God it's green so at least you can see it coming.

Junk food What on earth should you drink with a hamburger, cheeseburger, chicken nuggets, bargain bucket of fried off-cuts, blanched brontosaurus or any of the other palate-knackering, mass-produced, fast-food delicacies? A high-sugar, monstrously carbonated, brain-banging soft drink, of course, for that all-encompassing explosive gut/nauseous cold-sweat feeling that you look forward to enjoying ten minutes after racing this demonic cuisine down your cakehole. If you are seriously considering opening a bottle of wine (*Hello?*), you'll have to wrestle this toxic waste back into its day-glo polystyrene container and haul it back to your cave and now you've got to warm it up again! Do you bother? Course not, you're either starving or distinctly worse for wear, or both. But what should you uncork? Chilean Carmenère, entry-level Aussie

Shiraz/Cab, South African Chenin/Chardonnay (just keep the price down, you don't want to regret opening it in the morning). If you are well organised you'll always keep an 'emergency' white in the fridge and red in the cupboard for times like these. That way you can't open a serious bottle by mistake. Either way, while you are guzzling, Dante is hastily reworking his epic and inventing yet another circle of hell for your internal organs to slumber in overnight.

Kidneys Lambs' kidneys tend to absorb a fair amount of the flavour from the ingredients in which they are cooked, so follow those. Mustard is often used, so keep the reds firm, chunky and with a lick of crunchy, palate-refreshing acidity – Chianti, Morellino, Lagrein, Barbera, Montepulciano, Rosso Conero (all Italian), Rioja, Toro, Calatayud, Navarra (all Spanish), Languedoc-Roussillon and the Rhône Valley (both French) would all be worth a punt. (For *steak and kidney pie* see 'Beef'.)

Lamb Red Bordeaux is, strictly speaking, the classic combination with *roast lamb* or *lamb chops*. However, reds from nearby Bergerac or Madiran and, further afield, Burgundy, South Africa's smarter Pinotage and Shiraz, California's Merlot, Australia's Shiraz and Cabernet blends, Spain's Rioja, and Argentina and Chile's Cabernets and Merlots are all in with a very solid shout. Keep the wine firmly in the middleweight division and you will do well. You can, of course, go bonkers on the price or stick within a tight budget, as lamb is less particular than beef or game. The way it is cooked, though, should definitely influence your final choice. If cooked *pink*, the range of suitable wines is enormous (any of the above). If *well done*, then a fruitier style of red should be served, so head to the New World's treasure chest, as lamb tends to dry out and it needs resuscitation. Watch out for gravy and mint sauce, as an abundance of either could test the wine.

Lamb pot roast and casserole tend to be a little richer in flavour than a chop or roast lamb because of the gravy. Again, don't spend too much on the wine, as authentic Languedoc or southern Rhône reds will do fine. Shepherd's pie is incredibly easy to match. In fact, just open whatever you feel like – if it's red and wet, it will be spot on – a no brainer. Plain lamb shank is another relatively easy dish to match to red wine, with inexpensive European examples from Portugal, Spain, Italy and France all offering enough acidity and structure to cut through the juicy, mouth-watering meat. Moussaka, with cheese, onion, oregano and aubergines, is altogether different. Lighter, fruit-driven reds such as New World Pinot Noir, inexpensive workhorses from Toro, Alto Duero or Campo de Borja in Spain, or cheaper South American reds will work well. Stews like navarin (with vegetables), Irish stew, cassoulet or hot pot all have broader shoulders when it comes to reds. Beefier southern French examples from Fitou, Corbières, St-Chinian, Madiran, Faugères, Minervois or Collioure would be perfect. From further afield, Malbec from Argentina or Carmenère from Chile, as well as medium-weight, scented Aussie Shiraz (McLaren Vale, Pemberton or Yarra Valley) would also suit these dishes. Cold roast lamb follows the same rules as cold slices of beef and, to a certain extent, ham in that fruity, light reds and juicy medium- to full-bodied whites work pretty well. Beaujolais, served cool but not cold, is a great partner, while Chardonnay in any of the following guises would augment the dish – try medium-priced white Burgundy, Chardonnay from Margaret River, Adelaide Hills or Yarra Valley (Australia) or Nelson or Marlborough (New Zealand), or lighter South African and Chilean styles. Also, don't forget proper manly rosés – they are such an underrated drink, especially with cold cuts.

Lastly, *kebabs*, one of lamb's most exciting and gastronomically enlightening incarnations whether you've lovingly marinated and skewered the meat yourself or just adoringly watched it being shaved off that elephantine mass of meat in a kebab shop. I suspect you'd struggle to balance a kebab and a goblet of wine while stumbling down the street after a late-night gig but, on the off chance that you make it home before tucking into the nuclear-hot dish, a glass of big-brand, sub-fiver New World Chardonnay or Semillon/ Chardonnay would be a welcome break between mouthfuls. (And not something you'd be too upset about having opened in the cold, stark light of a new day.)

Liver *Calves' liver with sage* (an old-fashioned but ever-so-tasty retro dish) needs medium-weight reds with prominent acidity. The texture of medium rare liver is relatively delicate but the flavour is rich and pure, and the wine's acidity cuts through this intensity with style. Loire reds made from Cabernet Franc are your first port of call; Saumur-Champigny, Chinon, St Nicolas de Bourgueil and Bourgueil are all relatively inexpensive (sub-tenner) and a perfect match. Personally I wouldn't look any further but, if you need a larger choice, then head to northern Italy to some well known and other less so names – Valpolicella, Teroldego from Trentino, Lagrein, Marzemino and Cabernet (Franc or Sauvignon – sometimes Italians don't specify which you're getting). These all have the required fruit richness with the balancing acidity, freshness and grip needed for this task. *Liver and bacon* needs a touch more spice in a red wine, but not much more weight, so move to a warmer part of France or Italy (i.e. head further south or look for a hot vintage). Red Bordeaux and Chianti would be ideal, but this is likely to push the price up a few pounds.

Meat *Balls* (see 'Pasta'), *pies* (see 'Beef') and *loaf* (see 'Terrines').

Mexican *Fajitas, enchiladas, tortillas, quesadillas, tacos, burritos* (my tummy is rumbling, in a nice way) – loaded with chilli and salsa – lead to the consumption of copious quantities of lime-stuffed (I leave it out) beer. It may have excellent thirst-quenching properties but it's got bugger-all flavour. If you are partial to a glass of wine, you must go in search of ripe, fruity, chillable red grapes like Nero d'Avola, Negroamaro and Primitivo (from southern Italy), Carmenère and Merlot from Chile, inexpensive Zinfandel from California and Cabernet or Merlot cheapies from Oz to cool you down and smooth out your battle-scarred palate. As for whites – they are likely to get bashed up no matter what you choose, so find inexpensive, New World, mildly oaked Chardonnay or Semillon (or a blend of the two), chilled down to sub zero. Interestingly, *Cajun* cooking follows a similar pattern to Mexican when it comes to wine styles, as cayenne, paprika, oregano, garlic and thyme all cook up a storm and need to be tempered with similarly juicy whites and reds.

Mezze (or *Meze*) This is the chance for dry Greek whites to shine, and there are enough out there of sufficiently high quality to really hit the mark. If you are unable to track them down, then try dry Muscat, Pinot Blanc or Sylvaner from Alsace, New Zealand Sauvignon Blanc or Argentinean Torrontés. You could always try to find dry Muscat from Australia, Spain or Portugal, too. Albariño from northwestern Spain and good old Vinho Verde from Portugal also work well. Greek reds still lag behind the whites in terms of overall quality – some cheapies are fine, if a little coarse, but I would avoid spending more than a tenner as you will be hard-pushed to justify it. I would head off to the Mediterranean instead.

Mixed grill A vital part of every real man's cooking repertoire, mixed grill is the dish of choice for superheroes the world over. You need a rich, robust red and there is nothing more macho than a feisty southern Rhône (see the Gazetteer for top performers) or its New World counterpart, a 'GSM' blend (Grenache, Shiraz and Mourvèdre in any combo).

Moroccan/North African The most important factor to remember when matching this intriguing style of food with wine, is the level of spice involved in the dish. Once you have gauged this, you can do one of two things – either choose fresh, clean, neutral whites that sit in the background and let the food do most of the talking, or go head-to-head with the flavours and drink a stunning aromatic white. Spain, Italy and France are the most obvious and geographically closest ports of call and, within these three great wine nations, my favourite aromatic white styles would be Albariño (from Galicia in northwestern Spain), Viognier (south of France) and Ribolla Gialla, Traminer, Tocai, Lugana and richer Pinot Grigios (northeast and northwest Italy). Other Italian whites that would be a little more intriguing and competitive with the food are Grillo from Sicily, and Falanghina, Fiano and Greco from southern Italy. Reds that work well are Rioja or similar-style Tempranillo/Garnacha blends (Spain), chilled and ripe Côtes-du-Rhône (France), and Nero d'Avola, Aglianico or Primitivo (southern Italy and Sicily). If you want to go down the neutral route, choose Beaujolais as a red, or Alsace Pinot Blanc or Loire Sauvignon Blanc as a white. If you feel the need to stray further from the Med, aim for more Sauvignon Blanc, this time from Chile or South Africa, for its herbal, lime-juice characters, and Barossa Valley Bush Vine Grenache (South Australia) for its pure red-berry fruit and herbal, smoky nose.

Mushrooms Although mushrooms traditionally form an integral part of a vegetarian diet, I am delighted to forgo my rampant carnivorous tendencies if mushrooms form the backbone of an evening's cooking. The inbuilt 'meatiness' in field mushrooms or the intensity, flavour and texture of wild mushrooms really work for me. Clearly the mushroom family is a diverse one and you can cook them in every way imaginable, so this is a pretty long entry. When matching wine to mushrooms, ignore the fact that they are fungi and look at the task they are employed to do. *Baked* or *grilled* mushrooms usually retain their essence, moisture and flavour, and cellar temperature reds (i.e. chilled a touch) should allow them to express themselves. Make sure that you choose relaxed, fruit-driven reds with low tannins – simple Grenache blends, Gamay or Pinot Noir, for example. *Creamy sauces* are always difficult; if you overdo the cream, a robust, oaked Chardonnay or Semillon is needed, but if the cream features only in a supporting, 'whisked-in' role, then refreshing red grapes such as Merlot, Bonarda and Barbera would be superb. *Mushroom omelettes* and *mushroom tarts* are both classic examples of how a mushroom can hold its own in the competitive egg world – here, again, light, fruit-driven reds and smart, dry rosés must be mobilised. *Wild mushrooms* can be intensely scented, gamey and foresty, so look to my 'Game' entry and trade down in terms of muscle (and expenditure). *Mushrooms on toast* are ever-so fashionable again (hoorah) – good news, as there is nothing better for setting up your palate. This is one of the easiest dishes to make at home and, even if you splash out on fancy bread (Poilâne is surely the best in the world) and top shrooms, it is still dead cheap. Wine-wise, look to the main course you are preparing and downsize the wine a touch for your starters. If you are having a double serving as a stand-alone dish, then try Barbera or Dolcetto from northern Italy, for their truffley, black-cherry aromas and flavours. *Stuffed mushrooms* depend on what they are stuffed with. I know that sounds obvious, but cheesy or veggie ones work well with lighter reds. If you lose the cheese, rich whites are in with a shout – medium-sized Chardonnays and Rieslings are ideal. For *mushroom risotto* see 'Risotto'.

Mustard Make sure you turn up the volume on any red or white wine if you are contemplating a mustard sauce/dressing or an accompanying dish with a strong mustardy theme. You do not need to go too far in terms of size or style, but a notch up in quality and flavour is needed to accommodate the flavour intensity – this will probably mean you'll have to spend a pound or two more on your bottle.

Olives See 'Apéritif Wine Styles' if you are restricting your intake to pre-dinner olives. But, if you're cooking with olives, say in a lamb recipe, take care not to pour in the liquor (water, brine or oil) from the jar or can, as it is very pungent (and often not of the highest quality) and can cast too strong an influence over the final taste of the dish. This, of course, would affect you and your wine's chances of happiness. As usual, the trick is to look to the main ingredient in the recipe and make sure that your chosen wine can be enjoyed alongside a sliver of olive (munch on one and taste the wine as a road test). *Tapenade* is a funny old thing – totally unfriendly when it comes to wine (unless you find refuge in dry sherry), so it is best to go for very dry whites from cooler-climate regions, for example Frascati, Gavi, Soave, Lugana, Greco, Falanghina, Grillo and Vernaccia (all Italian), or Sauvignon de Touraine, Cheverny, Muscadet, Bergerac Sec, Jurançon Sec or Pacherenc de Vic Bilh (all French).

Onion As the leading ingredient in a dish, onion is at its best in a classic *French onion tart*, and Alsatian Riesling is the only true wine to drink with this noble offering. If you must stray from this advice (verbal warning from the wine police), Clare Valley Rieslings from South Australia would work beautifully. Occasionally you see *caramelised onions* offered as a side dish – watch out. They are often delicious, intensely sweet (of the same order as a treacle tart) and, although you can moderate this by combining mouthfuls with the other elements of your meal, they are a real danger to a glass of dry wine so don't bother drinking anything serious when you eat them. My advice is to munch enthusiastically and sip cautiously. For *French onion soup* see 'Soup'.

Oysters see 'Seafood'.

Paella Not worthy of its own listing, really, if it weren't for the fact that it is such a desperately cacophonous mix of ingredients. The answer is that chilled, ripe Cabernet Franc (red Loire), Albariño or Godello (Spanish white grapes) or French Grenache-based/Spanish Garnacha-based light reds and rosés all do well in a crowd-pleasing way.

Pasta *Naked* pasta tastes pretty neutral, which is why it is never served on its own. The trick with pasta-and-wine matching is to consider what you are serving over, under, around or in it. Stuffed styles such as *cannelloni, agnolotti, cappelletti, tortellini* or *ravioli* can contain veg, cheese, meat and all sorts, so think inside out and select accordingly. *Spinach and ricotta tortellini* soaks up juicy Italian reds like Freisa, Dolcetto and Barbera from Piedmont, and young, simple Chianti, Franciacorta, Bardolino and Valpolicella. *Seafood* pasta dishes, including the all-time favourite *spaghetti vongole* (clams), love serious, crisp Sauvignon

Blanc (from anywhere), decent Frascati (over £5 if you can find it!), Soave (again, break over the fiver barrier please), Lugana, Fiano di Avellino, Verdicchio, Greco di Tufo, Inzolia from Sicily and Vernaccia di San Gimignano.

Meatballs, spaghetti Bolognese, lasagne and meaty sauces all respond well to juicy reds. Keep the budget down and head for expressive, fruit-driven examples that work in harmony with the dish, as opposed to trying to dominate it. Consider all of Italy and many New World regions, but steer clear of overly alcoholic wines (read the label and stay under 13.5%). And, although heretical, anything bright and juicy made from Tempranillo or Garnacha from Spain would also be delicious. Roasted vegetables often pop up in pasta dishes, allowing you to choose between richer whites and lighter reds. Pesto may be a classic pasta partner but it is remarkably argumentative on the wine front. Oil, pine nuts, Parmesan and basil seem innocent enough, but put them together and you are forced into lean, dry whites for safety. Go to the famous Italian regions of Friuli, Alto Adige or Veneto as your guide. Sauvignon Blanc is made here, so at least you can rely on that stalwart grape but, otherwise, Pinot Grigio, Riesling, Picolit, Tocai Friulano, posh Soave and Pinot Bianco are all good bets. Red pesto is a funny old fish (not literally, of course). This time go for light red wines and keep their temperature down (15 minutes in the fridge) to focus the fruity flavours.

Cheesy and creamy sauces tend to be more dominant than the ingredients bound therein, so Bardolino and Valpolicella (both from Veneto), Dolcetto, Freisa and Barbera (all from Piedmont), Montepulciano (from Marche) and medium-weight Chianti (from Tuscany) are all accurate. If, for some reason, you want to stray from Italy's idyllic shores (I wouldn't – there is so much choice and the wines are great value and widely available), there is plenty to be found – medium-weight reds and dry whites are everywhere. Just remember not to overshadow the dish, particularly with higher-alcohol wines. For *tomato sauce*, see 'Tomato'. For *mushroom sauce*, see 'Mushrooms'.

Pâté Regardless of its main ingredients, pâté is, perhaps surprisingly, keen on white wines. The only reds that really work are featherweights such as Beaujolais and Bardolino. In the white world, you need to hunt down fruity, aromatic wines from any decent estate in my Gazetteer. The crucial character you are searching for, in terms of taste, is a degree of sweetness (not much, just a hint). All styles from the technically dry (but still ripe and fruity) Riesling, Gewürztraminer, Muscat, Chenin Blanc and so on, up to genuine rich/sweet wines can be considered. Pâté is usually served as a starter, so pouring a sweet wine at the beginning of the meal might seem a little about face. But if you are serving pudding or cheese later on in the proceedings (make sure you plan this carefully beforehand), you can happily open a bottle of sweet wine, serve a few small glasses for starters and finish it off later. Many sweet wines are sold in half (37.5cl) or 50cl bottles, so even if it's a small gathering, anything up to six, you'll not waste a drop.

Chicken liver pâté favours dry to medium-dry German Riesling, Alsace Riesling, Pinot Blanc or mildly sweet white Bordeaux styles (Loupiac or Saussignac) and older Aussie Rieslings (Eden and Clare Valleys). *Country pâté*, a clumsy catch-all term that often hints at a coarser texture pâté of indeterminate origin, similarly suits light white wines with a degree of sweetness (or a pint or two of real ale). If you are pushed into choosing from a short wine list or are confronted with an undernourished offie, then play safe, buy a dry white and hope for the best. But if you have the luxury of choice, then Alsace is a great region to start hunting.

Riesling and Tokay-Pinot Gris are the plum picks here. Head to the New World and you'll find Riesling in abundance in Australia, while Chilean Gewürztraminer is an unusual but rewarding style.

With *duck* pâté and *foie gras* (*goose liver* pâté), we are firmly in sweet wine territory – Sauternes, Loire and Alsace sweeties, Aussie botrytised Riesling and Semillon, or, on a tighter budget, Monbazillac, Ste-Croix du Mont, Loupiac, Cadillac and Saussignac (Sauternes' taste-alike neighbours). If you have never tasted this heady food-and-wine combo, you are in for a very pleasant surprise. *Parfait*, the smoother, creamier, Mr Whippy version of pâté, tends to reveal its covert brandy ingredient more than a coarse pâté, so make sure your wine is rich enough to cope with this. If you don't want to sip a sweet wine, then nearly sweet whites from Alsace also work. Vendange Tardive (late-picked) wines offer richness without cloying, sugary sweetness, and will appease the non-sweet wine fans. Grapes to consider are Tokay-Pinot Gris, Muscat, Gewürztraminer and Riesling. *Smoked salmon* pâté and other *fish* pâté incarnations are well served by dry aromatic whites (see 'Fish'). One thing to remember with pâté dishes is that occasionally *chutney* (or *onion confit/ marmalade*) is served on the side, providing an intense, sweet-fruit or veg explosion of flavour, which may confuse the wine. Alsatian Vendange Tardive wines, mentioned above, have tons of spice and richness of fruit, and they will simply cruise through these added flavours – dry wines will choke. I have already talked about *gherkins* and *capers* in the 'Charcuterie' section, so keep them well patrolled.

Peppers Fresh, crunchy, *raw* peppers crackle with zingy, juicy, healthy flavours. It should come as no surprise, then, that Sauvignon Blanc (from almost anywhere in the solar system) is the best grape for them – 'capsicum' is actually a recognised tasting note for this variety. It is a marriage made in heaven, but if you want to try something different, then dry Chenin Blanc from South Africa or Italian Pinot Grigio would also be splendid. *Piemontese* peppers are a favourite Saturday lunch dish of mine, and with the olive oil, garlic, black pepper and tomato ingredients, dry whites are required, especially if the traditional anchovy fillets are criss-crossed on top of the shimmering tomato hemispheres. Assertive Sauvignon Blanc is the best option, although Verdicchio, Orvieto, Greco, Fiano, Arneis and Gavi (or a less expensive, Cortese-based Piedmont white) would be appropriate. A *stuffed* pepper depends more on its stuffing than the pepper itself, so look to the filling for your inspiration. Generally speaking, meat or cheese stuffings go well with light Italian reds. Peppers *marinated in olive oil* love any dry white wines – for consummate accuracy Italian is best, so find some Soave, Frascati or Friuli single varietals such as Pinot Grigio, Pinot Bianco, Traminer or Sauvignon Blanc. For *gazpacho* see 'Soup'.

Picnics You simply must find screwcap-sealed bottles for picnics. And, thank goodness, there are so many out there these days. The benefits are numerous – there is no need for a corkscrew, you can reseal the bottle with ease and you also don't have to worry about anyone knocking it over. Your first port of call for all-round picnic-matching skills has to be rosé. It is multitalented when it comes to all manner of cold food dishes, and if you chill the bottles down ice cold before departure, it will drink like a fresh white early on and, as the day hots up (cross fingers), it will behave more like a red. This should cunningly coincide with your move through the courses, from crudités and dips, via smoked salmon, to rare roast beef and finally some good cheese. Other varieties that enjoy *al fresco* food are Sauvignon Blanc for whites and Beaujolais for reds. Once again, chill all of your wines right down prior to departure and drink them in order from white, via rosé to red, and bring some ice if you can.

Pigeon see 'Game' but spend less.

Pizza I adore pizza and, if prepared well, there is nothing to touch it for taste-bud satisfaction and that warm, pudgy-tummy thing afterwards (or is that just me?). Heroic pizzas rarely allow white wines enough space to be heard. However, I suppose a simple *vegetable* or *seafood* pizza might need a weedy, dry white wine. Assuming you have a tomato (or red pepper – much tangier) base and some mozzarella cheese on top, the real point of a pizza is the unlimited number of toppings that you sling on – *mushroom, onion, anchovy, caper, olive, beef, ham, egg, pepperoni* and, crucially, *chillies.* A real man's pizza has these and more, so you will have to find a feisty red and cool it down. My all-Italian, pizza-wine line-up includes: whites – Arneis, Soave, Bianco di Custoza, Verdicchio, Pinot Bianco, Pinot Grigio and Orvieto; chillable reds – Sardinian Cannonau, Freisa, Barbera and Dolcetto from Piedmont, Marzemino and Teroldego from Trentino, Bardolino and Valpolicella from Veneto and Chianti, Montepulciano d'Abruzzo, Morellino di Scansano, Sangiovese di Romagna, Primitivo di Puglia, Nero d'Avola di Sicilia, Negroamaro and Aglianico all from further south.

Pork The noble hog has so many different gastronomic guises that I have given the gallant sausage its own section. And, no doubt, *pâté* and *terrine* lovers are delighted that these two dishes warrant their own headings, as well. I have also dealt with *charcuterie, cassoulet, bacon, full*

English breakfast and *ham* in other sections – it just gets better! Here, though, I endeavour to cover the porcine dishes not otherwise mentioned. First the princely *pork pie* and its less exciting, ever-so-slightly oddly coloured, day-glo, asteroid cousin, the *Scotch egg*. A good pork pie is a real treat and, while I'm sure that a pint of Shepherd Neame ale is the ideal partner, a glass of Cru Beaujolais is also a perfect fit. The Scotch egg crops up in pub and picnic cuisine more than at the dinner table and bitter is the only sensible choice – but you wouldn't be putting a foot wrong by ordering a juicy Merlot either. If you like a dollop of Branston or piccalilli on the plate, then expect the wine to be sent into a momentary tailspin.

Chorizo and *salami* fall into the aforementioned 'Charcuterie' section, but remember that the spicier the salami, the greater the need for cool red wine. A plate of chorizo is excellent with dry sherry – manzanilla and fino are the two best styles. Next on the menu, *spare ribs*. Whether drenched in barbecue sauce or not, these are prehistoric fare, so Neolithic reds are needed to slake your thirst. Juice and texture are the essential ingredients, so head to the New World in search of Argentinean Sangiovese, Malbec, Bonarda or Tempranillo, Chilean Carmenère or Australian Cabernet/Shiraz blends. Californian Zinfandel would also work well, although it might be disproportionately expensive. *Rillettes*, which can also be made from duck or rabbit, expose one of pork's lighter sides. This mild, oddly fondanty, savoury dish is often served as part of a plate of cold meats. White wine is called for, with Pinot Blanc, Sylvaner and Riesling from Alsace all working well. As usual, Aussie Riesling will find this a doddle, too.

I have left the big daddy to last – *roast* pork. There are a number of ways to serve this so, when it comes to matching it to wine, the brief is fairly open. One thing is certain – if you are going to serve a red, make it light (Pinot Noir is best). Pork is far more excited by white wine, particularly if there is apple sauce sidling up to your plate. Classy, unoaked Chardonnay from Chablis or Burgundy would be exact, although New World Chardonnays can hack it so long as they are not overtly oaky. Riesling (dry and luxurious), Condrieu (the super-dear northern Rhône Viognier), Vouvray (make sure it says 'sec' on the label) and southern Rhône whites (thin on the ground but a lot of bang for your buck) are all worth a substantial sniff.

Quiche (and posh tarts) see 'Eggs'.

Rabbit Rabbit *rillettes* love a little more musk and exoticism in their wines than plain pork rillettes, so Marsanne, Roussanne and Viognier from anywhere in the world (Rhône is your starting point, maybe California or Eden Valley or Victoria in Australia next), or Pinot Blanc and Riesling (the richer styles from Alsace) would be mouth-wateringly spot on. For all other bunnies, hop along to 'Game'.

Risotto Generally, the richness and texture of a risotto needs to be 'cut' with the acidity of a clean, dry, white wine, but check what else you have folded into your risotto. It is these magic ingredients that matter the most when finding the perfect wine to counter the creamy, cheesy rice, particularly if you've whacked a spot of grated Parmesan, mascarpone and butter in with the stock! Light reds can work with *wild mushroom* risotto but I prefer scented, cool, classy whites. *À la Milanese*, with saffron, can force a light, dry white into submission unless it has enough fruit and 'oomph' – Arneis or Gavi from Piedmont are worth a go, as is Riesling from a good Australian or Alsatian producer. *Chicken and mushroom* risotto likes Chardonnay and light

Pinot Noirs, just as a non-risotto-style dish might. *Primavera* favours fresh, zingy, green whites – Sauvignon Blanc, anyone? Finally, *seafood* risotto – here dry Italian wines including decent Frascati, Vernaccia di San Gimignano, Arneis, Verdicchio Classico, Greco and Fiano, along with South African Sauvignon Blanc and Chenin Blanc make a rather delicious combination. Remember that Chilean Sauvignon is often cheaper than both South African and New Zealand versions, so if you are having a big risotto party then look here for a decent volume purchase.

Salads A huge subject that just needs a moment's common sense. Basic *green* or *mixed* salad without dressing is virtually tasteless, as far as wine is concerned. Be careful if it's dressed, though – particularly if vinegar is involved because this changes all the rules. *Seafood* salad enjoys the white wines that go well with seafood (obvious, I know, see 'Seafood'); *Niçoise* likes tangy Sauvignon Blanc, Sauv/Sem blends and neon green Margaret River or Hunter Valley Semillons (Australia); *chicken* salad works well with Rhône whites and middleweight Chardonnays; *feta* salad, not surprisingly, is perfect with dry Greek whites; *French bean and shallot* salad likes lighter, inexpensive Alsace Tokay-Pinot Gris and Pinot Blanc; *tomato and basil* salad is best matched with rosé or anything fresh, dry, keenly acidic, white and Italian; *Caesar* salad is great with Sauvignon Blanc, Grüner Veltliner (Austria) or Gavi; *Waldorf* salad needs softer, calmer white grapes like Pinot Blanc and Sylvaner (Alsace), or South African Chenin Blanc; *pasta* salad can get a little stodgy so uplifting, acidity-rich, dry whites are essential. Every country in the wine world makes salad-friendly wines, even the UK, where the better dry white grapes like Bacchus, Reichensteiner and Seyval Blanc, in the right hands, can be a joy (you know where to look!).

Sausages (Meaty ones, please, not fish or veggie!) Any sausage dish, including *toad-in-the-hole* and *bangers and mash*, needs manly, robust, no messin' reds. Cahors, Garnacha blends from Tarragona, Shiraz or Cabernet from western Australia, Victoria, Clare or McLaren Vale, Malbec from Argentina, any Languedoc or southern Rhône reds, Barbera from northern Italy, Primitivo from southern Italy, and Chinon or other red Loires are all suitable. Zinfandel, Merlot and Cabernet from California would also be awesome, as would a bottle of plain old red Bordeaux. Hurrah for sausages and their global compatibility with red wine! They're not fussy and nor should you be.

Seafood Muscadet, Cheverny, Menetou-Salon, Sauvignon de Touraine, Quincy, Pouilly-Fumé and Sancerre (all white Loire wines), Chenin Blanc (South Africa), Albariño (Spain), Lugana, Verdicchio, Soave and Pinot Grigio (Italy) and any buttock-clenchingly dry, unoaked New World whites are all perfect with seafood. *Squid* and *octopus* both need very dry whites with aromatic fruit, like Sauvignon Blanc, northern Italian or Penedès (Spain) whites, and resinous Greek whites if the dish is served in its ink. The curious, bouncy texture of both squid and octopus does not embrace wine in the same way fish does, so concentrate on the method of cooking and the other ingredients to help you make your final choice. Aussie Riesling is a must if you have a spicy dipping sauce.

Crevettes grises (the little grey/brown shrimps) eaten whole as a pre-dinner nibble, are stunning with Muscadet or Sauvignon Blanc from the Loire, Australia or New Zealand. *Crayfish* and *prawns* with dry English whites, simple, dry Riesling, and Sauvignon or Semillon/Sauvignon Blanc blends are all lovely. If you are a *prawn cocktail* fiend (a stunning dish if ever there was one), then decent Sauvignon Blanc (no need to spend over £8) is dry and sharp enough to wade through the livid pink Marie Rose sauce.

Lobster, the noblest of all crustaceans, served cold or in a salad, should tempt you to delve into the deepest, darkest corners of your cellar and uncork the finest whites. Burgundy (no upper limit), Australian (ditto) and Californian Chardonnay (only the best – not too oaky) and Viognier (from its spiritual birthplace in Condrieu) will all set you back a fortune but, hey, you've already bought lobster, so go the extra nine yards and finish the job properly. *Lobster thermidor* is not my favourite dish, as I feel that lobster loses its magical texture and elegant flavour when served hot, but you can easily uncork richer (but less expensive) whites like Aussie Semillons or South American Chardonnays. If you feel like a slice of lobster class, but for a slightly reduced price, then *langoustines* (or *bugs/yabbies* if you're mad for crustacea and on hols in Australia) are the answer. Lobster-wines are perfect here, but just adjust the price downwards by a few quid. *Dressed crab* is a fabulous dish and, once again, Loire whites like Muscadet (only £4 to £5 for a good bottle) are spot on. Dry whites such as Ugni Blanc from Gascony, Jurançon Sec and 'village' Chablis are also excellent, but again Sauvignon Blanc is probably the pick of the grapes (it always is). Don't just look at the Loire, though, as the white wines from Bordeaux and Bergerac often have a fair slug of Sauvignon in them and, of course, Sauvignon is grown all over the world.

Mussels probably do best in *gratin* or *marinière* form when dry Riesling, Barossa or Hunter Valley Semillon, New Zealand Pinot Gris and New World Sauvignon Blanc are all worthy contenders. *Scallops* require a little more weight in a white wine (mildly oaked Sauvignon Blanc; for example, Fumé Blanc from California). They can even handle a spot of light red or rosé (chilled). *Scallops sauté Provençal* (with tomatoes and garlic) and *scallops wrapped in bacon* are wicked with smarter rosé. *Scallops Bercy* (with shallots, butter, thyme, white wine, parsley and lemon juice) are superb with top Sancerre or Pouilly-Fumé – spend up, it will be worth it. *Oysters* are traditionally matched with Champagne – but not by me. I prefer a simple dry white like Muscadet, with its salty tang, or a 'village' Chablis or Sauvignon de St-Bris.

A *plateau de fruits de mer* involves all of the above, plus *whelks* (yuk) and *winkles* (mini-yuk), and really only needs a first-class bottle of Sauvignon de Touraine or Muscadet. You'll thank me when you receive the bill for this mountainous platter of seafood, as you'll only have spent a fraction of that on a bottle of chuggable wine. For *clams*, see 'Pasta'.

Side dishes see 'Vegetables'.

Snails see 'Garlic'.

Soups Dry sherry is often quoted as soup's ideal soul mate but it seems a little ludicrous to crack open a bottle of fino every time you fancy a bowl of broth. And, what's more, it isn't always the best wine for the job. The soup dynasty is a diverse collection of individuals – no one wine can expect to cover all of the flavours. *Minestrone*, with its wonderful cannellini bean base, and *ribollita* (the stunning, next-day minestrone incarnation – re-boiled with cabbage and bread thrown in for extra body) like to keep things Italian, with chilled Teroldego or Marzemino from Trentino and Valpolicella being superb candidates. If you want to hop over the mountains to France, then simpler southern Rhônes (a well-made C-de-R would do) make a refreshing and accurate alternative. *Spinach and chickpea* soup goes well with bone-dry whites like those from Orvieto, Frascati, Greco, Verdicchio (Italy), Penedès or Rueda (Spain), or Sauvignon Blanc from New Zealand, South Africa or Chile. *Vichyssoise* (chilled leek and potato soup) needs creamy, floral whites, such as straightforward Alsatian Riesling, South American or French Viognier, or light, white Rhônes.

Lobster or *crayfish bisque* has a creamy texture coupled with a deceptive richness, so dry sherry could conceivably make an appearance here. If you don't fancy that, then youthful white Burgundy is best. *Bouillabaisse with rouille*, the serious fish, garlic, tomatoes, onion and herb broth with floating toasty crostinis topped with garlic, chilli and mayo, is a mighty dish and yet it only needs very simple whites like our old favourites Muscadet and Sauvignon de Touraine.

Consommé is a definite Fino sherry dish (at last). *Gazpacho* (chilled *tomato, cucumber, onion, pepper* and *garlic* soup) likes nothing more than Spanish new-wave Viura (unoaked) or cheeky Verdejo from Rueda. *Mushroom* soup is another dry sherry candidate (you might use some in the recipe), while *French onion* soup goes well with dry Riesling from Alsace or South Australia. *Oxtail* demands hearty reds – rustic, earthy inexpensive southern French bruisers like St-Chinian or Minervois. *Lentil and chestnut* and *lentil and bacon* soups both crave dry sherry (this time trade up from a fino to an amontillado, for complexity and intensity). *Clam chowder* is basically a fishy soup with cream (and sometimes potato), so Sauvignon Blanc, Chenin Blanc and all seafood-friendly whites are perfect.

With *vegetable* soup, rustic reds at the bottom of the price ladder are needed. *Tomato* soup is a strange one. Always avoid oak. I favour light reds or dry whites – Gamay (Beaujolais or Loire) or Sauvignon Blanc (Pays d'Oc, Loire, South Africa or Chile) all do the job admirably.

Sweetbreads With *butter and sorrel*, *sauce ravigote* (mustard, red wine vinegar, capers and tarragon) or *sauce gribiche* (like ravigote but with chopped hard-boiled eggs and parsley as well), sweetbreads demand aromatic, decadently textured, luxurious, self-confident whites. Alsatian or South Australian Riesling (Clare or Eden Valley) with a bit of age would be my first choice. If you can't find any, then try creamy, oily, nutmeg- and peach-scented Rhône whites. All of these are dear, but there's no way around this quandary, as this is a demanding sector of the food repertoire. *Ris de veau aux morilles* (veal sweetbreads with a very rich, creamy wild mushroom sauce) needs the most intense Rhône whites or Alsatian Rieslings.

Tapas Sherry and dry white wines, preferably Spanish and avoiding oak, are perfect partners for these addictive Spanish snacks.

Terrines A terrine is a more robust, often hearty pâté, generally served in slices. So what's good enough for a pâté is often perfect with terrine. One of the classics is *ham and chicken*, and this loves white Burgundy or elegant, non-French, mildly oaked Chardonnays. Another white Burgundy lover is *jambon persillé*, the sublime parsley, jelly and ham dish. This is not surprising, as it is a Burgundian recipe in the first place. I would dive in with a youthful, inexpensive Bourgogne Blanc from a reputable Domaine, or head south to Rully, Mercurey, Montagny, Pouilly-Fuissé or a crisp Mâconnais wine for a match. Beaujolais, Alsatian Gewürztraminer, Riesling and Tokay-Pinot Gris love *rabbit*, *hare* and *game* terrines, particularly if there are prunes lurking within. *Fish* terrines follow the lead of fish pâtés and mousses with Sauvignon Blanc, Riesling, clean, fresh Chardonnays like Chablis, Fiano di Avellino from Campania in southern Italy and finally the enigmatic Spanish stunner, Albariño.

Thai Along the same lines as Vietnamese and other 'Asian but not overtly so' styles of cuisine, it is best to look to the main ingredient and then concentrate on appropriate southern hemisphere, fruit-driven wines. Likely candidates are: Australian or New Zealand Riesling, Viognier, Semillon, Verdelho, Pinot Gris and Sauvignon Blanc. New World sparkling wines in general work well, as do dry Muscats from Portugal and Pinot Gris, Torrontés or Viognier from Argentina.

Tomatoes Strangely, tomatoes are pretty fussy when it comes to wine matching (see 'Soup'). Pinot Noir works well and New World versions perform better than their Old World counterparts, as they often have more fruit expression and lower acidity. Other reds, like Sicilian Nero d'Avola, Aglianico, Primitivo (all southern Italy) and any juicy, warm-climate Merlot or Zinfandel would be accommodating. When *raw*, as in a salad, rosé or Sauvignon Blanc is a good choice. A *tomato sauce* demands dry, light whites and Italy is the best place to look for these, as they are often ripe and cheap. *Ketchup*, while delicious, is so sweet and vinegary that it gives wine a hard time. Use sparingly on your burger if you like drinking fine wine but drench it if you're gunning down a cheap glugging red.

Truffles Foresty, feral and musky – hoorah! Choose similarly scented wines to match this unusual life form – Burgundian Pinot Noir, Piedmont's magnificent Nebbiolo and Barbera, and Syrah (French and serious, please). If you want to cook chicken or fish with truffles, then vintage Champagne or top Alsatian or Australian Riesling would be spectacular (or go crazy and find some vintage rosé Champs).

Turkey The thing to watch out for with *roast* turkey is the cranberry sauce. Often a fresh, young Crianza Rioja or juicy New World Pinot Noir complements this outlandish red-fruit flavour. At Christmas, Aussie Grenache or Rioja is again a winner as mountains of cocktail sausages, bacon, sprouts and the rest take the flavour spotlight away from the turkey. If you are feeling very brave, totally ahead of your time, or just a little barking, then sparkling Shiraz from Australia (you can get a superb example for as little as £7) would be fantastic, celebratory and original. *Cold* turkey? See 'Chicken'.

Turkish I have already covered lamb kebabs (with lashings of chilli sauce) in the 'Lamb' section but, generally, Turkish food is best with Greek wines as the cuisine styles are linked, and the resinous, aromatic whites and purple, earth- and violet-scented reds are spot on.

Veal There are some mightily good dishes in this section but, sadly, there is no hard and fast rule as to what to follow on the wine front. In general, veal prefers to keep the company of grown-up white wines and classy, lighter reds. *Saltimbocca*, the terrific veal, sage and prosciutto dish, needs a wine to 'jump in the mouth'. Pinot Nero (Italian Pinot Noir) would be fine, but is hard to find and often a little dear. If your search is unsuccessful, try another unusual wine – Trincadeira from Portugal would be an inexpensive and inspirational substitute. *Vitello tonnato*, a phenomenal dish of contrasting flavours, using thinly sliced, braised veal and served cold, drizzled in a sauce made from marinated tuna, lemon juice, olive oil and capers, is one of the world's most sumptuous starters. Taking the tuna and anchovy (used in the braising stage) as your lead, fresh, sunny, seaside whites like Verdicchio, Greco and Vernaccia work especially well. If you are snookered for decent Italian whites, then go for a Kiwi Sauvignon. *Wiener schnitzel*, fried veal in egg and breadcrumbs, can often taste a little on the dry side, so see what else is on the plate. If there is nothing of enormous character to deflect your mission, give it the kiss of life with a juicy, mildly oaked Chardonnay. *Blanquette de veau*, the French classic with a creamy sauce, is definitely a white wine dish. Again, Chardonnay will do but for perfection go for Viognier, Roussanne or Marsanne blends from the Rhône or Victoria in South Australia. *Osso bucco*, veal shin with wine, tomatoes, parsley, garlic and zesty gremolata, is a lighter, yet headier stew than most. Tasmanian, Yarra Valley, Adelaide Hills (Aussie), New Zealand or Oregon Pinot Noir would be great, as would huge, full-on Chardonnays from anywhere in my Gazetteer.

Vegetables Vegetables (served on their own or as an accompaniment) taste, on the whole, relatively neutral. But, depending on how they are cooked, they can require a moment or two's thought on the wine front. Any *gratin* (vegetables baked with cheese) or *dauphinoise* (thinly sliced potato baked with cream and garlic) dish needs light reds or firm, self-confident whites.

Beetroot is a tad tricky, but Alsatian whites and cool, juicy reds generally have the texture and flavour to make it through. *Cabbage, leeks, spinach, parsnips, cauliflower, sprouts, courgettes, carrots, peas* and *potatoes* are usually innocent so don't worry about them, but *gnocchi* (plain or flavoured with spinach) needs juicy, fruit-driven wines with perky acidity to cut through their weird texture.

Marinated vegetables and *polenta* both love Italian whites – Pinot Grigio, Soave, Verdicchio etc. *Lentils* often dry the palate out and rustic, earthy reds are essential. Look to French Country wines for an endless supply of candidates or to Chile and Argentina for Malbec or Syrah/Shiraz. *Corn on the cob* is a dead ringer for New World Sauvignon Blanc. Open a bottle and, with some wines, you may actually detect a canned sweetcorn aroma! *Celeriac* is a stunning accompaniment to a dish and it has a pretty strong aroma and flavour, so make sure your wine is up to it.

Vegetarian If you are a strict vegetarian or vegan, look at the label (usually the one on the back), as most organic and vegan associations have stickers or a logo to let you know the contents and production techniques of the wine. If you are still unsure, ask your wine merchant.

Vinaigrette A passion killer for wine, vinegar is strongly flavoured and makes any wine taste flat for a few seconds. This can give your palate an annoying stop-start sensation. Dressing made with lemon juice and oil is more wine-friendly – and healthier!

Vinegar See above! Balsamic vinegar seems to be more accommodating than most (perhaps because you tend to use less), and it is more winey in depth and flavour.

Welsh rarebit Ah – what a good note to finish on! Whether you make these toasties for late-night nibbling or as a traditional savoury to serve after pudding, you deserve a meaty, rustic red swimming alongside. Anything from the south of France, southern Italy or Spain would be a delicious match – make sure it is not too dear. And if you are really broke, pop over to Australia for a chunky, inexpensive Shiraz.

PUDDINGS

It is pretty obvious that port drinking has taken something of a hit recently in the after-dinner-drinking stakes. Fashion is a cruel thing. Many of my friends now prefer to end a feast on a sweet wine, as it enlivens the palate and wakes you and your taste buds up. For my part, there is nothing better than finishing off dinner with a glass of sweet wine, particularly if it accompanies a tasty pudding. Thankfully there is only one rule to remember when matching wine to sweet dishes – you must make sure the wine is at least as sweet as the pudding, otherwise it will taste dry. Most wine shops have a few sweet wines lurking on the racks, but sadly not as many as one would like. You may have to find a decent independent merchant to get a good selection of sweeties so check out the Directory on page 217 for a merchant near you. But also run through my Top 250 for a serious list of sweet wines that, between them, cover every dish in this decadent section.

Almond tart Despite its heavenly flavour and fantastic texture, this dish needs careful handling on the wine front, as an overbearing sweet wine would crush the delicate almondy nuances. Lighter, youthful sweeties like Muscat de Beaumes-de-Venise, Muscat de Rivesaltes, Moelleux (sweet) Loire whites and Jurançon Moelleux would all be spot on. Stick to these styles if your almond tart has fresh fruit on top. *Bakewell tart*, while perhaps not as elegant as a fresh fruit tart, likes these sweeties, too, but you'd be well advised to go for a little more age on a sweet Loire wine or head to Australia for a similar styled botrytised Semillon.

Apple *Strudels*, *pies*, *fritters* and *crumbles* all come with varying degrees of nutty, cinnamony, buttery pastry and burnt-brown-sugar flavours. These overlay the intrinsic fruitiness of the filling and, therefore, demand a richer, heavier style of pudding wine than you might expect. Having said that, we are still in the foothills of sweetness! German Riesling (of at least Auslese status), late-picked Muscat or Riesling from Australia, classic French Sauternes (don't blow too much dosh) or New World botrytised Semillon and lighter, youthful Hungarian Tokaji (a lower number of puttonyos, say 4) are all runners. *Baked* apples (assuming they are served warm/hot) ought to have ice-cold, light, fresh German or Austrian Riesling (Spätlese or Auslese level) and clean, light Muscats. This will give your palate a marvellous and invigorating sauna then plunge-pool sensation every time you take a sip. If they are served cold, don't bother with wine. See below for *tarte tatin*.

Apricot A sensationally accurate apricot match is Vendange Tardive (late-picked) Condrieu (from the northern Rhône) so look there for apricot *crumble*. Unfortunately this wine is extremely rare and exceedingly expensive (best to buy it on hols in the Rhône). Where else should you look? Australia makes some good copies and they look great. Another answer is sweet Jurançon (Moelleux), bursting with tropical quince and peach flavours, or Monbazillac or Saussignac – a friendlier-priced Sauternes-style offering from southwest France.

Bananas *Raw* – I hope you're joking! *Banoffee pie*, the hideous love-sprog of sticky toffee pudding and banana pennies, can only be tamed by the most outrageous of sweet wines – Hungarian Tokaji (although I wouldn't waste it), Australian liqueur Muscat (this will slow you down, hee hee) and Malmsey Madeira (I might even turn up if this was served). With banana *splits*, the candied sprinkles, shaky-shaky things and ice cream flavours are more dominant than the neutered banana, so watch out on the wine front – I'd head straight for the Aussie liqueur muscat.

Berries *Black*, *goose*, *blue*, *rasp*, *berri-berri* (bad joke), *logan*, *huckle*, *straw*, *Halle* (good joke), *mul*, *cran*, *bil* and his amoureuse *damson* bounce around in many different recipes. Whether they are served au naturel, in a juicy *compote*, or cooked in a *summer pudding*, they all love the talented sweet wine superhero Semillon and his trusty sidekick Muscat. Track down these grapes from France – Sauternes, Saussignac, Monbazillac, Loupiac and Cadillac all fall neatly into the Semillon camp; while Muscat de Rivesaltes, de Beaumes-de-Venise, de Frontignan and de Lunel all advertise Muscat on the label, so are easier to spot on the shelves. Aussie late-picked Muscats are all great and inexpensive, but watch out for liqueur Muscats, as they are wildly different and will destroy a delicate *fruit purée*. Not that you'd care if you were drinking that, as you'd be a giggling wreck in the corner!

Biscuits/Biscotti (and proper shortbread)
Vin Santo is the top choice for the extended biscuit family. Sweeter Madeira styles and good old cream sherry also work very well, counter-pointing the crumbly texture, butter and fruit or nut ingredients well. None of these wines need be served in large quantities (unless you are feeling particularly gung-ho), as they are all sipping styles. Sauternes (heady, sweet white Bordeaux) or New World botrytised Semillon (exactly the same style but better value) come in a worthy second. Other lighter biscuits enjoy the company of simple sweet wines – I would still stick to Semillon- or Chenin Blanc-based French versions.

Brandy snaps God, I love brandy snaps (I thank my lucky stars for Ma Jukesy – I wouldn't stand a chance trying to make them myself without visiting Casualty). Once again, try Australian liqueur Muscat, you'll love it – just stop when you've got through the first batch and bottle, otherwise you'll be drunk, fat and lock-jawed in no time.

Bread and butter pudding You need wines with a bit of power and acidity to stand up to a traditional B & B pudding (so I am told, as this dish is really not my scene). Weightier Muscat-based wines are just the job – Moscatel de Setúbal from Portugal and Moscato or Passito di Pantelleria from the volcanic island off the south of Sicily would be there or thereabouts. Take it steady, though, as these are addictive, gloriously moreish and hugely alcoholic. Buckle up for a late night.

Cakes What's wrong with a cup of Rosy Lee? Well, quite a lot, really, when you could be enjoying an elegant glass of cream sherry (with your vicar) or a schooner of Aussie liqueur Muscat with your *coffee* cake (and the WI), Bual or Malmsey Madeira with *Dundee* or *Battenberg* (and your grannie), Maury or Banyuls with a traditional *fruitcake* or *brownies* (and the Brownies), or demi-sec Champagne with *Victoria* (Beckham) or *lemon sponge*. For the perfect sugar hit try *doughnuts* (no lip-licking) with ice-cold Asti and a very good friend.

Cheesecake Whether it is cherry or any other style, the 'cheesiness', not the fruit, controls the choice of wine. Botrytised Semillon and Riesling from the New World, Coteaux du Layon and other sweet Loire wines, Austrian Beerenauslese, and Alsatian Vendange Tardive Riesling and Tokay-Pinot Gris all work. The trick is to keep the sweetness intense and fruit-driven, without resorting to heavyweight styles of high alcohol/fortified wines.

Cherries In *pie* form, cherries behave like berries and prefer the company of mid-weight sweet wines. Served with *chocolate* in a *marquise* or *Black Forest gâteau*, though, and they can handle a much richer wine. Try Amarone, the wickedly intense red Valpolicella from Veneto in Italy, Maury or Banyuls from Roussillon (France) or really juicy Californian Zinfandel for a bizarre match. Your guests might think you're a course late with the red but it works, honest.

Chocolate A deluxe choccy *cake* can, if it's not too intense, retreat into lighter Muscats and botrytised Rieslings. Chocolate *mousse* (knock off the antlers), *petits pots au chocolat* and chocolate *soufflé* all head towards Orange Muscat, with its wonderful pervading aroma and flavour of orange blossom. This is one of the finest food-and-wine combinations of all, as orange and chocolate are natural partners (just ask Dawn French). Australia and California make two examples that I know of, so well done Brown Bros and Andrew Quady respectively, your places in the choccy hall of fame are guaranteed. If these wines are too hard to find, then you could even twist my arm to open a bottle of Asti Spumante! Chocolate *pithiviers,* the single most decadent dish in the pudding repertoire, need unctuous fortified wines with a touch of burnt nuttiness – Banyuls or Maury (Roussillon, France), liqueur Muscat and liqueur Tokay (Australia). Match any of these ridiculously insane dishes with the following list of galactically serious wines – Passito di Pantelleria (for its mind-boggling orange zest aroma), Tokaji, black Muscat (space-age – get ready for re-entry), liqueur Muscat, PX (short for Pedro Ximénez, the boozy, black, teeth-rottingly sweet turbo-sherry), botrytised

Semillon from the New World, Maury and Banyuls (the mega, port-like sweet Grenache wines from the south of France) and, finally, young, punchy, underrated, tawny port.

Christmas pudding During the festive period, it is useful to have a wine that lasts well once opened – you've got to make it all the way from Christmas Eve to New Year's Day, after all. Top-quality tawny port and liqueur Muscat or Tokay from Australia, as well as heady Malmsey Madeira, all fit the bill. You can squeeze twelve glasses out of a bottle without short-changing anyone. Not bad, hey, and these are not expensive wines by any stretch of the imagination. See my Top 250 for this year's worthy versions.

Cinnamon rolls A heavenly creation – but ever so wicked. You need considerable levels of sweetness and toffeed aromas in the wine to cope with the intensity of sugar. Vin Santo, Hungarian Tokaji, liqueur Muscat and old oloroso sherry would be stunning. Old-fashioned *lardy cakes* are hard to find these days, sadly, but if you do know a dealer, then stick to Malmsey Madeira – it fits with the image as well as being a great flavour combination.

Crème brûlée As I only like the crunchy, caramelised bit on top, as opposed to the silky, creamy bit, I have asked some pals for their advice on this one. The general consensus is that you need to aim somewhere between my almond tart and cheesecake wines. As Loire sweeties, made from Chenin Blanc, appear in both sections, they must be spot on – Coteaux du Layon (and that extended family), Vouvray Moelleux, Bonnezeaux (pronounced 'Bonzo') and Quarts de Chaume are your choices. You could always look for some South African Chenin Blanc sweet wines, as the grape is widely planted down there and they are stunning value.

Crème caramel Sadly this is another pud that you won't get me near (I've got a real texture issue with this dish – too slippery), but I have it on good authority that light, delicate sweeties are required. German Auslese Rieslings from the Mosel and youthful, fairy-light Muscats are apparently spot on.

Crêpes Suzette Clairette de Die, the little-known sparkling wine from the Rhône, or Asti (Italy's frothy Moscato) would be cheap but worthy options, with demi-sec Champagne being the grown-up, expensive choice.

Custard As soon as you start waving custard around, you are giving your palate much more to think about. Intense creaminess craves acidity in a wine. With custard being the ultimate in eggy creaminess, the big guns like Malmsey Madeira, liqueur Muscat and Tokaji must be got out of the cellar.

Doughnuts see 'Cakes'.

Figs I'm feeling too naughty to concentrate on this one – sorry! What is it with me and figs? [I don't think we want to know! Ed]

Fruit *Raw* fruit of any kind has a much lighter flavour than you would expect when pitted against a sweet wine. So stay with dainty Asti, German or Austrian Spätlese Rieslings, demi-sec Champagne, fresh, clean Muscats, Italy's Recioto di Soave, Spain's Moscatel de Valencia or very light, young Sauternes. But if you fancy a *lychee*, then find a sweet Gewürztraminer, as it has remarkable lychee characteristics on the nose and palate. *Poached* fruit, like *peaches* or *apricots*, picks up sweetness from the added sugar and can be pretty intense, so tread carefully. You may need a rich Coteaux du Layon from the Loire to see you through.

Fruitcake see 'Cakes'.

Gingerbread A wonderful creation that, along with *ginger cake* and *ginger biscuits*, is made even better when accompanied by a glass of good-quality cream sherry, Bual or Malmsey Madeira.

Gooseberry fool A heavy, oleaginous sweet wine would trample all over this refreshing, palate-priming pudding. What you need is young, botrytised Semillon, like Sauternes, Saussignac, Monbazillac or Loupiac, or Asti or demi-sec Champagne. Try to keep the price down, as more expensive wines will usually taste finer and more intense. Or grab a bottle of fresh, young Riesling Auslese (Mosel, Germany) for a fruit-cocktail, grapey flavour – it will also be much cheaper.

Ice cream If you want to play safe then *vanilla*, *chocolate*, *rum and raisin*, *coffee*, *chubby-hubby* and *cookie-dough* ice creams all love Pedro Ximénez (PX – it makes good body paint … apparently!). You could always try sweet liqueur Muscats from Australia as well. If you have a *fruity* ice cream or *sorbet*, just leave it alone – you need a few minutes without a goblet in your hand occasionally. If you want to ignore me then go crazy and experiment, but you're on your own.

Jam tart You have to find a very sweet wine. This is the only rule, as you can't get sweeter than jam. Icewine from Canada might be a relatively inexpensive way of tackling this dish. Other than that, you are looking at a monstrous price tag (Trockenbeerenauslese from Germany, for example) and, you have to ask yourself, is the tart worth it?

Jelly Light, sweet German Riesling would be alright. Hang on a sec – there can't really be someone thumbing through this chapter looking for the 'wine with jelly' entry!

Lemon meringue pie German or Alsatian Riesling would work well here. Make sure it's sweet but not too cloying. Recioto di Soave (Italian) or youthful sweet Loire Chenin Blanc (Coteaux du Layon) would also handle this citrus theme very well. The good thing is that these styles of wine are relatively inexpensive and pretty easy to come by. *Tarte au citron*, my preferred choice in the lemon/pastry arena, is also stunning with Coteaux du Layon.

Meringue Flying solo, meringues are virtually tasteless (and dusty) so knock yourself out (not literally) and experiment. If served with fruit (*pavlova*), it's the fruit that you need to worry about so see 'Fruit'.

Mince pies I generally follow the Christmas pud/Christmas cake lead of rich, sweet Madeira, youthful tawny port and blindingly brilliant Australian liqueur Muscats. It will save you another trip to the shops and all of these brews are big enough to wrestle with a four-star brandy butter.

Pastries Belonging in the same school as tarts and cakes, I am not really convinced you need a wine recommendation for this family of buns and so on. Are you really going to crack open a bottle of wine for a *pain au chocolat*? You are? Well, don't let me stop you – demi-sec Champagne, Coteaux du Layon, Muscat de Beaumes-de-Venise, Saussignac and Monbazillac are France's best efforts. Botrytised Riesling from Australia and New Zealand, or sweet Muscat from California might also work well.

Otherwise, try a German Spätlese Riesling but remember to keep the price down – and wait for midday!

Peach melba Botrytised Riesling does the peachy thing well, as you should be able to detect peach notes in the wine – head Down Under or to Germany. Alternatively, a late-picked Viognier from the Rhône would be stunning, but they are hard to come by and mightily dear. If all else fails, grab a bottle of Sauternes, as it is the most multi-talented of all sweet wines.

Pecan pie A great dish that craves the company of Australian wines. Not sure why but this is exactly the right fit and you should search for a liqueur Muscat of Tokay. If this sounds a little too much like globetrotting, stick with a posh-tasting but inexpensive Malmsey Madeira.

Pineapple upside-down pudding This deserves a mention as one of the classic and most irresistible menu items of all time (well, I think so anyway!). The caramel and pineapple team up to form a supremely exotic partnership and smart Sauternes would give a real result here. If you are keeping an eye on expenses, then Australian botrytised Semillon would also work wonders.

Plum crumble Of the crumble family, plum is up there with blackberry and apple as one of the mightiest. A degree of concentrated sweetness is needed here, so head off to Canada for decadent Riesling Icewines, Hungary for sexy Tokaji, or Italy for heroic Vin Santo.

Rhubarb A relative lightweight compared to plum crum, rhubarb *crumble* takes it easy on the wine front. Exotically sweet Riesling from just about anywhere has rhubarby notes on the nose and palate, so this is the one and only grape to follow with rhubarb–based puddings (including *fool*, *compote* and *ice cream*).

Rice pudding Still nothing to add to this note. I haven't eaten rice pudding since school, and don't intend to.

Rum baba As its name suggests, a rum baba has a bit of a kick to it. Underneath the mild, genial exterior, a sweet-wine-thumping freak is itching to get out. Rum baba is the Hannibal Lecter of the pudding world and you have to go for a fortified wine to stand a chance of survival. Our SWAT team are tawny port, Bual or Malmsey Madeira and liqueur Muscat. Night sights on ... go get 'em boys.

Sorbet see 'Ice cream'.

Steamed puddings I am a devout fan of steamed puddings. The greatest syrupy, toffeed, old-fashioned ones (*spotted dick*, *treacle sponge* and *suet pudding* included) deserve the most regal sweet wines. I don't care that suet is a beastly ingredient and that these recipes don't involve any tricky cooking techniques. To me they are culinary utopia. They may have been mentioned before but, all these wines do the business, so here we go – top-flight botrytised Semillon (from anywhere), decadent Madeira, Tokaji (spend up by as many puttonyos as you can afford), Vin Santo (see the Gazetteer) and liqueur Muscat (from any one of the top Victorian or South Australian specialists in Australia).

Strawberries Top quality strawberries love Asti and Moscato d'Asti (Italy), demi-sec Champagne and Clairette de Die (Rhône, France). These are all fizzy or frothy, with the faintest touch of grapey sweetness.

Tarte au citron see 'Lemon meringue pie'.

Tarte tatin This is another of the greatest dishes of all time. I haven't put it into the apple section – not because these days tatin is made with pear and all manner of other fruit (and savoury ingredients – I saw a beetroot one the other day! Why?), but because the tatin method of cooking is the influencing factor. The rich, toffee/caramel gooeyness is what preoccupies the palate and, for that reason, honeyed Loire sweeties like Coteaux du Layon are right on the money. New World botrytised Semillons would be great as well, and Sauternes would be a real treat.

Tiramisù A strangely unappetising dish, in my opinion, as coffee, mascarpone, chocolate and brandy are frighteningly odd teammates. If you must eat this sickly dish, stay accurate with Vin Santo (to knock the flavour out) or Marsala (to knock you out).

Treacle tart Treacle tart, particularly if you have included lemon zest in the recipe, is not as stodgy as you might expect. You could try Sauternes but, if in any doubt, Hungarian Tokaji, Vin Santo or youthful liqueur Muscat would probably be safest.

Trifle The grand, old English creation, adorning vicarage sideboards up and down the country, must be delighted to have so many options on the wine front. German Riesling Beerenauslese is my top choice but any sweet Riesling would be lovely. Likewise, Sauternes and the family of worldwide sweet Semillons all love this dish. If you are going to pour in a bit of booze (sherry is traditionally used), a good quality cream sherry is probably best. Whatever you choose, I'll have a large glass of pud wine and politely refuse the trifle.

Zabaglione Passito di Pantelleria, from an island off Sicily, is the only wine to accompany this creamy concoction – unless the Marsala you use in the recipe is of sufficient drinking quality. If it is, then you can cover two bases with one wine – and that must be the epitome of food-and-wine matching.

CHEESE

The old 'red-wine-with-cheese' adage is downright wrong. When pondering which wine to drink with your chosen cheese, keep an open mind as, surprisingly, almost anything goes – white, red, sweet, dry and fortified. Try to keep your cheese board simple to limit the number of flavours and, therefore, wines needed – and watch out for chutney as its pungent flavour tends to trip wines up. I have listed the main categories of cheese and mentioned, within each, some of my favourite examples.

Fresh cheese (*Cream cheese, feta, ricotta* and *mozzarella*) These usually pop up in salads or simple cooking and their flavours are not dominant, so drink what you fancy. Whites would be best but make sure they have some cleansing acidity on board.

Natural rind cheese (*Goats' cheese – Crottin de Chavignol, Sainte-Maure de Touraine, Saint-Marcellin* and *Selles-sur-Cher*) Sauvignon Blanc from the Loire Valley in France is the benchmark wine to drink with goats' cheese, and the stunning bottles from Sancerre are the pick of the crop (Chavignol is one of the finest wine villages in Sancerre and the home of the famous Crottin de Chavignol cheeses). If you're caught short, though, any dry, fresh, unoaked white would be fine. If you feel like drinking red, then Gamay, Beaujolais or Loire Cabernet Franc work perfectly well.

Soft white cheese (*Camembert, Brie de Meaux, Pavé d'Affinois, Chaource, Bonchester, Pencarreg, Explorateur, Boursault, Gratte-Paille* and *Brillat-Savarin*) Once again, Sauvignon Blanc works terrifically well here. Although, if you want more palate 'oomph', head to Marlborough in New Zealand, Elim in South Africa or Adelaide Hills in Australia. Remember that the richer the cheese, the bigger the white, so Chardonnay can be considered, too. For reds try Pinot Noir (either red Sancerre or lighter red Burgundies), fresh young Syrah/Shiraz from the Rhône or McLaren Vale in Oz, and rosé Champagne. Gratte-Paille and Brillat-Savarin traditionally go well with youthful, inexpensive red Bordeaux – stick to my favoured wines in the Gazetteer section or Top 250.

Washed rind cheese Milder examples like *Chaumes, Port Salut* and *Milleens* need nothing more than dry, fruity reds – light Loire examples, inexpensive red Bordeaux or New World Merlots. Smellier cheeses, including *Epoisses, Chambertin* and *Langres*, really enjoy white Burgundy (from Chablis in the north all the way down to Mâcon in the south), Alsace Riesling or Tokay-Pinot Gris, and other controlled (i.e. not too oaky) Chardonnays from further afield. *Munster* loves Alsatian Gewürztraminer and *Vacherin Mont d'Or* loves red Burgundy, Beaujolais and lighter red Rhônes.

Semi-soft cheese This covers a huge selection of cheese. Try the following combinations: *Livarot* – Alsatian Tokay Pinot-Gris; *Maroilles* – Roussanne or Marsanne from the

Rhône; *Pont-l'Evêque* – Viognier, also from the Rhône; *Raclette* (assuming you are reading this halfway up a mountain in the Alps, you lucky thing) – anything from the Savoie region, red or white; *Gubbeen* – Pinot Blanc or Sylvaner from Alsace; *Edam* – light whites and reds or whatever, it's not fussy; *Morbier* – Rhône whites; *Fontina* – light, Alpine Gamay or Valpolicella; *Reblochon* – this outstanding cheese likes much richer Gamay (smart Cru Beaujolais) and also red Burgundy; *Saint-Nectaire* – another heroic cheese, particularly the wild, farmhouse version, likes the same again, plus meaty red Côtes-du-Rhônes; *Tomme de Savoie* – Rhône whites or lighter reds; *Bel Paese* and *Taleggio* – Lombardy whites such as Lugana and reds like Dolcetto, Barbera and Franciacorta.

Hard cheese This is the largest category of all, ranging from mild, via medium and strong, to extra-strong cheeses. As a starting point get an idea of the strength and age of your chosen cheese (a small taste in the shop is recommended) and this will help your wine selection. Cheeses in this group are, among others – *Cheddar*, *Gruyère*, *Cheshire*, *Parmigiano-Reggiano*, *Pecorino*, *Cornish Yarg*, *Double Gloucester*, *Lancashire*, *Caerphilly*, *Gouda*, *Beaufort*, *Manchego*, *Cantal*, *Etorki*, *Comté*, *Emmenthal*, *Jarlsberg* and *Mimolette*. Listing wines in order from those for mild cheese all the way to wines for the extra strong: whites – Alsace Pinot Blanc, Chablis, Jurançon Sec, white Burgundy, white Rhônes, New World Semillons and, lastly, New World Chardonnays; reds – Loire reds, Chilean Merlot, Côtes-du-Rhône, spicy Italian reds like Primitivo, Old World Cabernet from Bordeaux or Margaret River (Australia), Shiraz from Frankland, Barossa Valley, McLaren Vale and Clare Valley (Australia), Vino Nobile di Montepulciano and Chianti (Italy), and

Zinfandel (California); fortified – port (tawny, LBV and vintage), Madeira, Banyuls and Maury (both from France), and old oloroso sherries.

Blue cheese For *Stilton*, look no further than rich, nutty Madeira, tawny port, LBV or vintage port; *Roquefort* and *Fourme d'Ambert*, however, prefer sweet Sauternes, Monbazillac or Saussignac; *Gorgonzola* likes Amarone della Valpolicella; *Chashel Blue* needs sweet whites; *Dolcelatte* is a bit of a lightweight and, because of its unusual sweet flavour and texture, I never eat it so can't help you; and, finally, *Beenleigh Blue* needs a pint of authentic, hazy scrumpy cider (drunk in Oxford overlooking the Cherwell!).

GAZETTEER

GRAPE VARIETIES

Before I launch into the hot list of my favourite wineries in the world, I have compiled a short Albariño-Zinfandel of the most important white and red grape varieties in the world. These are the chaps that make most of the wines in this guide and you will see their names mentioned in many of the write-ups in the Top 250. These tasting notes should give you an idea of some of the vast array of flavours you will find in the wines.

WHITES

Albariño/Alvarinho (Al-ba-reen-yo/Al-va-reen-yo)

A top-notch example will have a peachy aroma like Viognier and a floral, spicy palate like Riesling. They always have a tangy, bone-dry, refreshing finish, often with a touch of spritz.

Aligoté (Alee-got-ay)

Aligoté produces dry, lean apéritif styles of wine designed for drinking within the first year or so of release.

Chardonnay (Shar-dunn-ay)

Ranging in style from pale, neutral and characterless to wildly exotic, rich and golden – you should be able to detect honey, butter, freshly baked pâtisserie, hazelnuts, vanilla, butterscotch, orange blossom and fresh meadow flowers in full-on Chardonnays.

Chenin Blanc (Shuh-nan Blon)

Chenin is an underrated grape that makes clean, zippy, dry, apéritif wines; medium-dry, textured, food-friendly styles; and rich, honeyed, succulent peach-flavoured sweeties dripping in unctuous, mouth-filling richness.

Gewürztraminer (Guh-vurz-tram-inner)

'Gewürz' has the most distinctive aroma of any grape variety. Pungent lychee, spice and rose petal abound on the nose, and the palate is usually oily, rich and intense. The finish varies from bone dry to just off-dry, and they often have the unusual knack of smelling sweet but tasting dry.

Manseng (Man-seng)

Both Gros and Petit Manseng wines have a complex nose of quince, peach and lemon curd, and a citrusy, floral palate usually accompanied by a shockingly firm, crisp finish. Although pretty rare, these grapes are also used to make celestial sweet wines with juicy, tropical, honeyed flavours.

Marsanne (Marce-ann)

Plump, rich, vaguely floral, peachy and always oily, Marsanne makes rather hefty, foody wines and likes to be blended with the more elegant grape Roussanne.

Muscat (Muss-cat)

Muscat wines vary from the lightest, fizziest soda-siphon of grapey juice, to the deepest, darkest, headiest liqueur that looks like a rugby player's liniment and tastes like knock-out drops. Muscat is the only grape variety that in its simplest form actually smells and tastes 'grapey'.

Pinot Blanc/Pinot Bianco (Pee-no Blon/Pee-no Bee-anko)

Almost all PBs worldwide are unoaked, dry and relatively inexpensive. They taste vaguely appley, creamy and nutty. Most are dull but every now and again a delicious one comes along with more weight and intrigue.

Riesling (Rees-ling)

One of the truly great white varieties, Riesling produces a vast array of wine styles, from aromatic, bone-dry apéritifs, through structured, lime-juice-scented, foody beauties, via long-lived, complex, off-dry stunners, and ending up at heart-achingly beautiful sweeties. Rhubarb, petrol, honey, citrus, honeysuckle and spice are there in varying degrees throughout this cornucopia of guises – heavenly.

Roussanne (Roo-sann)

Generally lean, leggy and hauntingly aromatic with hints of apricot and honey. When on top form, Roussanne takes well to oak barrels and can provide a welcome change for Chardonnay drinkers.

Sauvignon Blanc (So-veen-yon Blon)

'Sauv' Blanc is an up-front, brazen, aromatic, happy-go-lucky style, with an asparagus, fresh herb, lemon and elderflower scent, and refreshing, zesty, dry, citrusy fruit on the palate. Sauvignon is the definitive apéritif grape variety.

Sémillon (Sem-ee-yon)

The dominant aromas in dry Sémillon are honey and lime juice, and sometimes creamy vanilla and toasty oak elements creep in, depending on the style of wine. But Sémillon also makes incredible, unctuous sweet wines, tasting of tropical fruit, honey, honey and more honey.

Tokay-Pinot Gris/Pinot Gris/Pinot Grigio (Tock-eye Pee-no Gree/Pee-no Gree/Pee-no Gridge-ee-oh)

The flavour of Tokay-Pinot Gris is somewhere between that of Pinot Blanc and Gewürztraminer. The distinctive nose of this grape is one of spice, fruit and honey. It does not have the rose-petal, perfumed element of Gewürz, and tends to be drier, like Pinot Blanc. Italy's Pinot Grigio is more akin to Aligoté, as it usually makes a light, spritzy, dry, apéritif style of wine.

Viognier (Vee-yon-yay)

In the best examples, Viognier offers a mind-blowing perfume of peach kernels, wild honey and apricot blossom, followed by an ample, curvaceous body with plenty of charm and a lingering, dry aftertaste.

REDS

Cabernet Franc (Cab-er-nay Fron)

Often used in a blend with Cabernet Sauvignon and Merlot, Cabernet Franc gives an aromatic dimension to a red blend. On its own it has firm acidity, oodles of black fruit flavours and a wonderful violet element coupled with green, leafy notes on the nose.

Cabernet Sauvignon (Cab-er-nay Soe-veen-yon)
Age-worthy Cabernet Sauvignon forms the backbone of many sturdy, lusty reds. Its hallmarks are deep colour, blackcurrant flavour, with occasional cigar-box or cedarwood notes. When it's on top form, a smooth, velvety, dark-chocolate texture and flavour emerge from the glass.

Gamay (Ga-may)
Gamay is a jolly fellow that makes underrated, early-drinking wines ranging in taste from chillable, frivolous, summery, strawberry juice concoctions to wintry, foody, black cherry and cracked-pepper styles.

Grenache/Garnacha (Gre-nash/Gar-natch-ah)
Grenache is usually blended with Syrah (Shiraz) among others. It is a meaty, earthy, red- and black-fruit-drenched variety, often with high-ish alcohol and a garnet hue. It sometimes picks up a wild herbal scent not dissimilar to aromatic pipe smoke.

Malbec (Mal-beck)
This brutish grape is inky black in colour and loaded with macerated black-fruit flavours and earthy spice, often enhanced by a dollop of well-seasoned oak. Malbec is one of the biggest, brawniest red varieties on the block. Also known as Cot in Cahors.

Merlot (Mer-low)
Merlot is a juicy red grape, with supple, smooth, silky, blackberry, plum, red-wine-gum and fruitcake flavours. It happily flies solo but loves the company of Cabernet Sauvignon in a blend. As Merlot is usually oak aged, the fruit flavours are often accompanied by a touch of sweet, wood-smoke barrel nuances.

Mourvèdre/Monastrell/Mataro (More-veh-dr/Mon-ah-strell/Mat-are-oh)
This rich, plum- and damson-flavoured variety is often made

into powerful, earthy, long-lived wines. It is not the most charming variety in its youth but ages gracefully, picking up more complex aromas and flavours along the way. It also likes to be blended with Grenache and Syrah.

Nebbiolo (Neb-ee-olo)

A tough grape that often needs five years in the bottle to soften to drinkability. A great Nebbiolo can conjure up intense plummy flavours with leathery, spicy, gamey overtones and a firm, dry finish.

Pinotage (Pee-no-tahge)

Pinotage is an earthy, spicy, deeply coloured grape with tobacco and plums on the nose, crushed blackberry fruit on the palate and a hearty, full, savoury finish. A speciality of South Africa.

Pinot Noir (Pee-no Nw-ar)

When on form, the Pinot Noir nose is often reminiscent of wild strawberries, violets and redcurrants, with a black-cherry flavour on the palate. There can be a degree of oakiness apparent, depending on the style. As these wines age, they may take on a slightly farmyardy character and the colour fades to pale, brick red.

Sangiovese (San-gee-o-vay-zee)

This grape has red- and black-fruit (mulberry, cherry, plum, blackcurrant and cranberry) nuances on the nose with a whiff of fresh-cut herbs and leather for good measure. Famous for making Chianti, there is usually an oaky element tucked into the wine, and it always has an acidic kick on the finish.

Syrah/Shiraz (Sirrah/Shirraz)

Syrah invokes explosive blackberry and ground-pepper aromas with vanilla, smoke and charred-oak nuances. In the New World, big, inky-black Shiraz (the Syrah synonym) often has high alcohol and a mouth-filling prune, chocolate, raisin and spice palate.

Tempranillo (Temp-ra-nee-yo)

Ranging in flavour from vanilla- and strawberry-flavoured early-drinking styles, to dark, brooding, black-cherry reds, Tempranillo is Spain's noblest red grape, and the main grape variety in Rioja and countless other serious Spanish wines.

Zinfandel (Zin-fan-dell)

'Zin' tastes like a flavour collision between turbo-charged blackberries, a handful of vanilla pods and a fully stocked spice rack. These wines generally have luxurious, mouth-filling texture and often pretty scary alcohol levels.

WINE REGIONS OF THE WORLD

In this crucial chapter I have taken my lifetime's tasting notes and whittled them down to the very best bodegas, Châteaux, Domaines, estates, tenutas and wineries. This year, as always, I have augmented this list with brand new finds, but also subjected the existing roll call of heroes to a thorough inspection. Each and every entry has had to fight for its place in this elite list, and this year it's the biggest yet – a good sign that more people are making better wine than ever before.

If a favourite winery of yours is missing, it is either because I haven't yet tasted their wines or, sadly, they have not quite made the cut. Please do drop me a line if you have a hot tip (see address on page 255) and I will track down the wines and make sure I have a go before next year's edition. There are no one-hit-wonder estates in this list, only top-quality, talent-rich, hard-working wine-making experts, whose bottles have set my palate alight with wonder and enthusiasm. These are the producers you can rely on day in, day out, when you are shopping for home drinking, eating out in a restaurant, travelling the globe on business or holiday, or buying a gift for a wine-smart friend.

Occasionally you'll spot a producer or winery whose name is in bold. These are specially selected estates that are truly outstanding and every wine in their entire portfolio is first class. If a producer is both in bold and has a £, it means that its wines are on the expensive side (£25 plus). These titanium-plated names are money-no-object wines, for those of you with a no-upper-limit mentality. This doesn't mean that every wine they make is out of reach – far from it. Their flagship wine may be dizzily dear, but their other labels may still be brilliant and significantly cheaper, so do take note. The bold estates without a £ make more affordable wines (somewhere between £5 to £25), so keep an eye out for them – this is where I do virtually all of my everyday drinking.

ARGENTINA

The fifth largest wine producer in the world still has a lot of work to do to convince me that they are heading in the right direction. Progress seems slow – reds, on the whole, are big, muddy and over oaked. There are only a handful of wines here that I feel I can't live without – this is not a very good score compared with other countries. I have no doubt, though, that in the £5 to £10 mark Argentina has some hearty reds. The Malbec and Bonarda grapes are two very good reasons to go shopping in this section of your offie. But, beyond that, there is massive competition out there for the other international red grapes. As far as whites are concerned, I would favour Chile's wines unless you fancy a glass of the intriguing, indigenous Torrontés grape. This may sound harsh, but Argentina needs to raise its game to be taken seriously on a world stage. A little test – how many Argentinean wines are there on your favourite restaurant's wine list? See!

The best Argentinean estates are – **Anubis**, Argento, **Bodega Noemía de Patagonia**, **Catena Zapata (Catena)**, **Clos de los Siete**, **Familia Zuccardi**, Finca El Retiro, Lurton, **Norton**, **Santa Julia**, Terrazas, Valentin Bianchi and Weinert.

AUSTRALIA

I visit Australia more than any other winemaking country in the course of my work. On each and every trip I discover more exceptional and mind-blowing wines. So exciting is the current state of the Australian wine scene that I was inspired to launch my very own annual Aussie wine initiative – the 100 Best Australian Wines (www.matthewjukes.com).
This is a celebration of the very best wines that make it over to our shores. The vast majority of Australian wines sold in the UK are everyday drinking bottles at below the £5 mark. The speed and accuracy with which Australia tackled the UK market with these wines was astounding. This sector of sales is the main reason why Australia is number one in the UK. My aim is to drag the average wine lover up the ladder to where I think Australia really rules the roost – £6.99 to £14.99. With the exception of very few grape varieties, Australian wines are shoulder to shoulder with the very best in the world at this level, and it is these wines that we should start to embrace.

In sheer value for money terms I think that it is very hard to beat the Aussies at this game. There are of course exceptions, and you will find loads in the Top 250, but as a nation, they are fast becoming not so much the new kid on the block, as the model to which all others have to aspire.

Why is this? I think that the answer lies with the people working within the business. The passion, excitement, determination, business acumen, palate awareness and their sheer finger-on the-pulse-of-modern-society mentality is nothing short of phenomenal. Add to that world-class viticulture and cutting edge technical wizardry (embracing screwcaps so quickly is one way that Australia and New Zealand lead the world) and the picture becomes clearer. But the final element, which tips the scales in favour of this enchanting land, is the liberal dusting of fun that you find in the bottle, and also in each and everything these winemakers do. This simple yet fundamental ingredient is something that a vast chunk of the rest of the wine world simply fails to realise is key to making great wine. It is Australia's recipe for success.

From the big brands at the bottom of the ladder, who make some of the most popular wines on our shelves, to the more serious offerings featured in this book and beyond, Australia is making terrific in-roads into our cellars. Being number one is not good enough, though. Australians are continually striving to make better and better wines – this should send a shiver down competitors' spines. I am lucky enough to travel the world and I don't see this hunger for improvement anywhere else. It is not all success of course, as part of this development is a willingness to admit defeat if something goes wrong and then to have the determination to start again immediately, developing a new label, flavour or concept.

This positive momentum does not just happen on a winery-by-winery basis. It happens in a very big way, too, as each region has its own generic body promoting its wines and sharing its hard-earned knowledge among its members. This collaborative mentality means that everyone benefits from shared experiences and they move forward together. This is one of the reasons Italy, Spain and France have lost out to Australia of late. They not only find it hard to work with their neighbours but, in most cases, they actively don't want to!

An emergence of cooler-climate wines packed with finesse and elegance is one of the strong moves of late. Big, flabby, oaky Chardonnays have all but disappeared off the shelves. Huge, heady, high alcohol reds are also starting to evolve into finer, more balanced creatures with tempered muscle and calmer oak. Crisp Sauvignons are popping up everywhere and Cabernet Sauvignon seems to be enjoying something of a comeback. Australian Riesling is one of the finest value styles of wine on the planet and you can't find better value Shiraz anywhere. You can even buy sparkling wine that kicks Champagne's arse for half the price – all of this would have sounded crazy five years ago! These days you would be hard pushed to find better quality/price ratio wines anywhere else in the world.

I am working night and day to find the greatest wines on the planet. I love my job and don't mind wading through hundreds of duff bottles if a good one pops up eventually. The fact is I have a higher hit rate of stunning bottles in Australia than in any other country in the world. This is an irrefutable fact. And I also drink more Aussie wine at home than any other country, too.

There is an entire world of wine to be discovered in Australia and this is the definitive list of wineries. They will not let you down.

WESTERN AUSTRALIA
The top producers are – Alkoomi, Amberley, Ashbrook Estate, Brookland Valley, **Cape Mentelle**, **Cullen**, **Devil's Lair**, Evans & Tate, Ferngrove, Forrest Hill, **Frankland Estate**, Garlands, Goundrey, **Houghton**, Howard Park, Juniper Estate, **Leeuwin Estate**, Millbrook, **Moss Wood**, **Picardy**, **Pierro**, Plantagenet, **Suckfizzle Augusta (Stella Bella)**, Vasse Felix, **Voyager**, West Cape Howe, Wignalls, Willow Bridge and Xanadu.

SOUTH AUSTRALIA

The top producers in each region are:

Clare Valley – Annie's Lane, Cardinham, Clos Clare, Crabtree, **Eldredge**, **Grosset**, Jeanneret, **Jim Barry**, **Kilikanoon**, Knappstein, **Leasingham**, **Mitchell**, **Mount Horrocks**, **Neagles Rock**, O'Leary Walker, Paulett, **Petaluma**, Pikes, Reilly's, Sevenhill, Skillogalee, Taylors (Wakefield in the UK), **Tim Adams**, Two Fold and **Wendouree £**.

Barossa Valley – Barossa Valley Estate, Burge Family Winemakers, Charles Cimicky, **Charlie Melton**, Chateau Tanunda, Craneford, Elderton, **Fox Gordon**, **Glaetzer**, **Grant Burge**, **Greenock Creek**, **Haan**, **Heritage**, Hobbs, **Kaesler**, **Leo Buring**, Massena, Murray Street Vineyards, **Orlando (Jacobs Creek)**, **Penfolds**, **Peter Lehmann**, Rockford, Rolf Binder Wines, Rusden, **St Hallett**, Saltram, Seppelt, **Spinifex**, **Standish Wine Co.**, Teusner, Thorn-Clarke, Tin Shed, **Torbreck £**, **Turkey Flat**, **Two Hands**, **Willows**, Wolf Blass and **Yalumba**.

Eden Valley – Heggies (Yalumba), **Henschke**, **Irvine**, **Mesh (Grosset & Hill Smith)** and Pewsey Vale (Yalumba).

Adelaide Hills – Ashton Hills, **Barratt**, Chain of Ponds, **Geoff Weaver**, **The Lane (Edwards Family)**, **Nepenthe**, Petaluma, **Shaw & Smith** and **TK (Tim Knappstein Lenswood Vineyard)**.

Adelaide Plains – **Primo Estate** and Wilkie.

McLaren Vale – **Bosworth**, Cascabel, **Chalk Hill**, **Chapel Hill**, Chateau Reynella (Hardys), Clarendon Hills, **Coriole**, d'Arenberg, Fox Creek, **Gemtree**, Geoff Merrill, **Hardys Tintara**, **Hastwell & Lightfoot**, Hoffmann's, **Kangarilla Road**, **Kay Brothers Amery**, Koltz, **Linda Domas**, **Mitolo**, **Noon**, Oliver's Taranga, Pertaringa, Pirramimma, Richard Hamilton, Rosemount (McLaren Vale), Simon Hackett, Tatachilla, **Ulithorne**, **Wirra Wirra** and Woodstock.

Coonawarra – **Balnaves**, Bowen, Brand's, Highbank, **Hollick**, Jamiesons Run, **Katnook**, Ladbroke Grove, **Leconfield**, Lindemans, **Majella**, **Parker**, **Penley**, **Redman**, **Wynns** and **Yalumba**.

Miscellaneous – Ballast Stone (Currency Creek), Bleasdale (Langhorne), Brothers in Arms (Langhorne), **Heartland** (Limestone Coast/Langhorne), **Tapanappa** (Wrattonbully) and Zonte's Footsteps (Langhorne).

VICTORIA

The top producers are – **All Saints**, **Baileys**, Balgownie, **Bannockburn**, **Bass Phillip**, Battely, **Best's Great Western**, **Bindi**, By Farr, **De Bortoli (Yarra Valley)**, Brown Brothers, **Campbells**, Castagna, **Chambers Rosewood**, Cobaw Ridge, **Coldstream Hills**, Craig Avon, **Craiglee**, **Crawford River**, Curlewis, **Dalwhinnie**, David Traeger, Diamond Valley Vineyards, **Domaine Chandon (Green Point)**, **Domaine Epis**, Dromana Estate, **Gembrook Hill**, **Giaconda £**, Hanging Rock, Heathcote Winery, Jasper Hill, **Kooyong**, McPherson, **Main Ridge**, Métier Wines, **Mitchelton**, **Morris**, Mount Ida, **Mount Langi Ghiran**, **Mount Mary**, Passing Clouds, Pondalowie, **Provenance**, Redbank, **Savaterre**, Scorpo, **Scotchmans Hill**, **Seppelt Great Western**, Sorrenberg, Stanton & Killeen, Stonier, **Tahbilk**, Tallarook, Taltarni, Virgin Hills, Water Wheel, Wild Duck Creek, Yarra Burn, **Yarra Yering**, **Yeringberg** and **Yering Station**.

TASMANIA

The top producers are – Andrew Pirie, Apsley Gorge, **Bay of Fires**, Chatto, **Clover Hill**, **Craigow**, **Domaine A (Stoney Vineyard)**, Elsewhere, **Freycinet**, Grey Sands, **Jansz**, No Regrets, **Pipers Brook (Ninth Island)**, Providence, Spring Vale, **Stefano Lubiana** and Touchwood.

NEW SOUTH WALES

The top producers are – Allandale, Bimbadgen, Bloodwood, Brangayne, **De Bortoli (Riverina)**, **Brokenwood**, **Clonakilla**, Cumulus, Glenguin, **Keith Tulloch**, **Lake's Folly**, Lark Hill, Lillypilly, Lindemans, Logan Wines, McGuigan, **McWilliam's/ Mount Pleasant**, Meerea Park, Rosemount (Hunter Valley), Simon Gilbert, Tempus Two, **Tower Estate** and **Tyrrell's**.

AUSTRIA

Austria is currently riding a wave of (unlikely) popularity in the UK press. The Austrians and their lovely wines cannot seemingly do a single thing wrong. Now I don't want to stick a branch in the spokes of this freewheeling nation and its delicious bottles, but while I love funky Rieslings and zesty Grüner Veltliners, I do baulk at having to spend well over a tenner for the pleasure. Only recently have we seen decent producers' wines at around the £7 mark with goodish distribution in the UK. In this respect they are light years behind the competition. But, because they are not Germany (even though they make Riesling and the bottles and names look similar), they make dry, crowd-pleasing white wines and somehow we have an emotional attachment to the idea of Austrian wines (although I am not sure why), they will continue to do well. My advice is to stick to my list below and mind out for inevitable price-vertigo.

The top producers are – Alois Kracher, **Bründlmayer**, **Emmerich Knoll**, **Feiler-Artinger**, **Franz Hirtzberger**, Fred Loimer, Freie Weingärtner Wachau, Graf Hardegg, G & H Heinrich, Helmut Lang, Hiedler, Höpler, Josef Pöckl, Jurtschitsch, **Manfred Tement**, Paul Achs, **F.X. Pichler**, Polz, **Prager**, Salomon, Schloss Gobelsburg, Sepp Moser, Velich, Wieninger, Willi Opitz and Dr Wolfgang Unger.

CANADA

It has been another year of distinct inactivity from the Canadians, and, to be honest, you would have go there on holiday to find a decent list of wines, because we in the UK, only ship wine from a handful of estates.

The best estates are – **Burrowing Owl**, **Cave Springs**, **Château des Charmes**, Daniel Lenko, Henry of Pelham, **Inniskillin**, **Mission Hill**, **Osoyoos Larose**, Paradise Ranch, Quails' Gate, Southbrook, Spring Cellars, **Sumac Ridge** and Tinhorn Creek.

CHILE

With a new generic marketing body in the UK, things are finally starting to happen with regard to Chilean wine. Whether this will actually improve the quality of the wines we see on the shelves remains to be seen, but at least the wines are becoming more visible and accessible. All of the Chileans I know seem to be working hard, and results are starting to come through with more regularity, but I still think there is a ton of competition on the international stage. Chile has seemingly taken over from Australia as the source of reliable, sub-£4 red and white wine – but do they really want this thankless job? My advice is to follow the fine estates below and vary your Cabernet and Merlot diet accordingly. Don't forget about Carmenère, the coffee bean and sweet pipe-smoke-scented red grape and keep your eyes peeled for new, cooler regions coming on stream with finer, more balanced wines. Whites tend to be better at the low or no oak end of the spectrum.

The best Chilean estates are – **Alvaro Espinoza**, **Amayna**,

Antiyal, Araucano, Casa Lapostolle, Concha y Toro
(Casillero del Diablo, Marqués de Casa Concha, Terrunyo,
Don Melchor), Cousiño Macul, De Martino, Michel
Laroche & Jorge Coderch, Miguel Torres, San Pedro,
Santa Rita, Seña, Valdivieso, Veramonte, Viña Errázuriz,
Viña Haras de Pirque, Viña Leyda, Viña Montes, Viña
MontGras, Viña Morandé, Viña Pérez Cruz and Viñedos
Organicos Emiliana.

FRANCE
BORDEAUX
I realise that most top end red Bordeaux falls into the
pant-wettingly scary price bracket (there are £ signs
everywhere in this section) and they also usually need a
decade under their belts to really start off on their
drinking curve, but there is no getting away from the fact
that this is one of the most important and influential wine
regions in the world. When these châteaux get it right
(i.e. the weather is kind and there's no rain at harvest),
the wines are hard to beat. I am always sadistically tough
on this list each year, as I have no time for lightweights or
fashion-conscious emperor's new clothes styles of wine.
The bottles that rock my boat are the stellar estates,
whose wines can't be copied anywhere else on the planet
and whose flavours transport your palate to a different
dimension. Bordeaux is the home to the majestic red
grapes Cabernet Sauvignon, Merlot and Cabernet Franc.
The percentages of each grape variety in the final blend
vary from château to château, depending on the sub-
region, soil and winemaker. The wines will also have spent
eighteen months or so maturing in smart, French oak
barrels. This classic recipe is the model for red wines
around the globe. *Bonne chance mes amies!*

RED WINES

THE LEFT BANK

Graves Bahans-Haut-Brion £, **Carmes-Haut-Brion**, Chantegrive, **Domaine de Chevalier**, de Fieuzal, Haut-Bailly, **Haut-Brion £**, **La Mission-Haut-Brion £**, Pape-Clément, Picque-Caillou and Smith-Haut-Lafitte.

Haut-Médoc and **(Bas) Médoc** Arnauld, Cambon la Pelouse, de Lamarque, Malescasse, Patache d'Aux, **Potensac**, Rollan de By, **Sociando-Mallet**, Tour du Haut-Moulin and Villegeorge.

Margaux d'Angludet, Brane-Cantenac, Cantemerle, **Durfort-Vivens**, Ferrière, d'Issan, La Lagune, **Margaux £**, **Palmer £**, Pavillon Rouge du Château Margaux and Rausan-Ségla.

Moulis and **Listrac Chasse-Spleen**, Clarke, Fourcas Loubaney and **Poujeaux**.

Pauillac Batailley, **Les Forts de Latour**, **Grand-Puy-Lacoste**, Haut-Bages-Libéral, Haut-Batailley, **Lafite-Rothschild £**, **Latour £**, **Lynch-Bages**, Mouton-Rothschild £, **Pichon-Longueville Baron £**, **Pichon-Longueville-Comtesse de Lalande £** and Pontet-Canet.

St-Estèphe Beau-Site, Le Boscq, **Calon-Ségur**, **Cos d'Estournel £**, Cos Labory, Haut-Marbuzet, La Haye, Lafon-Rochet, **Montrose £**, Les-Ormes-de-Pez, de Pez and Ségur de Cabanac.

St-Julien Clos du Marquis, **Ducru-Beaucaillou £**, **Gruaud-Larose £**, Lagrange, **Langoa-Barton**, **Léoville-Barton £**, **Léoville-Las-Cases £**, **Léoville-Poyferré £**, St-Pierre and Talbot.

THE RIGHT BANK

Canon-Fronsac and **Fronsac** Canon-Moueix, **de Carles**, Fontenil, du Gaby, Hervé-Laroque, Mazeris, Moulin-Haut-Laroque and La Vieille-Cure.

Castillon d'Aiguilhe and Puyanché.

Côtes de Bourg and **Blaye** Haut-Sociando, Roc des Cambes and Tayac.

Lalande-de-Pomerol Bel-Air, Belles-Graves, La Fleur de Boüard and Laborde.

Pomerol Beauregard, Bon Pasteur, **Certan Marzelle**, Certan-de-May, **Clinet £**, Clos de Litanies, Clos du Clocher, Clos René, **La Conseillante £**, **La Croix-St Georges**, Domaine de l'Eglise, **l'Eglise-Clinet £**, l'Enclos, **l'Evangile £**, La Fleur de Gay, **La Fleur-Pétrus**, Le Gay, Gazin, **Hosanna**, **Lafleur £**, Lafleur-Gazin, Latour à Pomerol, Petit Village, **Pétrus £**, Le Pin, **Trotanoy £** and Vieux-Château-Certan £.

St-Emilion Angélus £, L'Arrosée, **Ausone £**, Beau-Séjour Bécot, Belair, Canon-La-Gaffelière £, Le Castelot, **Cheval Blanc £**, Clos Fourtet, Dassault, La Dominique, Figeac, Larmande, Magdelaine, Monbousquet, Tertre-Rôteboeuf £, La Tour-du-Pin-Figeac, **Troplong-Mondot £** and Valandraud £.

DRY WHITE WINES
Carbonnieux, **Clos Floridène**, **Domaine de Chevalier £**, de Fieuzal, **Haut-Brion £**, **Laville-Haut-Brion £**, **Pavillon Blanc de Château Margaux**, **Smith-Haut-Lafitte** and La Tour Martillac.

SWEET WHITE WINES
Sauternes and **Barsac** d'Arche, Bastor-Lamontagne, Broustet, **Climens £**, **Coutet £**, Doisy-Daëne, Doisy-Dubroca, Doisy-Védrines, de Fargues, Filhot, **Gilette**, **Guiraud**, Les Justices, **Lafaurie-Peyraguey £**, de Malle, Nairac, Rabaud-Promis, **Raymond-Lafon £**, Rayne-Vigneau, **Rieussec £**, **Suduiraut £**, **La Tour Blanche £** and d'Yquem £.

BURGUNDY

My favourite wine region in the world is home to the most

incredible Chardonnay and Pinot Noir on the planet. I visit Burgundy several times a year – for work and for pleasure. I simply adore the wines, the food and the people. But, and this is very important, just because this is the most hallowed turf in the wine world, it doesn't mean that some reprobates don't make some dross here, too! Unless you have this failsafe list of top domaines in your hand, you could very seriously (and very expensively) lose your way. Burgundy is a veritable minefield of tiny vineyards and thousands of producers – French inheritance law at its peak of confusion! Pick carefully and use my vintage table at the back of this guide, too, and you will be fine – I promise. Every other estate in the world tries to reach the heights of Pinot Noir and Chardonnay perfection that they achieve here in Burgundy. They can't – this soil and setting are unique. Some come close, but these vineyards are extremely special – one visit and you'll see why. It is easy to get hooked! You will also find the zippy white grape Aligoté and much-derided red variety Gamay (Beaujolais) in Burgundy ably support the two aforementioned super-grapes. Stick to these chaps and you can eat and drink without busting the bank, but only for lunch mind you, as it's back to Pinot and Chardonnay for dinner! What follows is worth its weight in Grand Cru Pinot Noir – the ultimate list of Domaines. This list will, I guarantee, unlock the code to the most enigmatic wine region of all. Remember me when you gaze into your next glass of celestial Burgundy!

CHABLIS
Chablis (white) **Billaud-Simon**, A & F Boudin, Daniel Dampt, des Genèves, Jean Durup, **Jean-Paul Droin**, **Laroche**, **Laurent Tribut**, Louis Michel, **Raveneau £**, **René & Vincent Dauvissat** and William Fèvre.
St-Bris-le-Vineux and **Chitry** (white) Jean-Hugues Goisot.

CÔTE DE NUITS

Marsannay-la-Côte and **Fixin** (mainly red) Bruno Clair, Charles Audoin, Fougeray de Beauclair and René Bouvier.

Gevrey-Chambertin (red) **Armand Rousseau**, Bernard Dugat-Py, **Claude Dugat**, **Denis Mortet**, Drouhin-Laroze, **Fourrier**, Géantet-Pansiot, **Joseph Roty** and Sérafin.

Morey-St-Denis (red) **Dujac**, Hubert Lignier, **des Lambrays**, **Ponsot** and **Virgile Lignier**.

Chambolle-Musigny & Vougeot (red) Christian Clerget, **Comte Georges de Vogüé**, **Ghislaine Barthod**, Jacques-Frédéric Mugnier, Pierre Bertheau, **G. Roumier** and **de la Vougeraie**.

Vosne-Romanée and **Flagey-Echézeaux** (red) **Anne Gros**, **Emmanuel Rouget**, **Jean Grivot**, Lamarche, **Leroy £**, **Méo-Camuzet £**, Mongeard-Mugneret, René Engel, **Robert Arnoux**, **de la Romanée-Conti £** and Sylvain Cathiard.

Nuits-St-Georges (red) Alain Michelot, Bertrand Ambroise, **J-C Boisset**, Daniel Chopin-Groffier, Daniel Rion, **Dominique Laurent**, Faiveley, Henri Gouges, Jean Chauvenet, Jean-Jacques Confuron, Lécheneaut, **Nicolas Potel** and **Robert Chevillon**.

CÔTE DE BEAUNE

Ladoix (mainly red) Edmond Cornu.

Aloxe-Corton and **Ladoix-Serrigny** (mainly red) Michel Voarick.

Pernand-Vergelesses (red and white) **Bonneau du Martray (Corton-Charlemagne) £**, Dubreuil-Fontaine and Maurice Rollin.

Savigny-lès-Beaune (red and white) Chandon de Briailles, **Jean-Marc Pavelot** and Maurice Ecard.

Chorey-lès-Beaune (red) Germain and **Tollot-Beaut**.

Beaune (mainly red) Bouchard Père et Fils, A-F Gros & François Parent, Joseph Drouhin, **Louis Jadot** and Maison Champy.

Pommard (red) **Comte Armand**, **de Courcel**, **Jean-Marc Boillot** and Parent.

Volnay (red) Coste Caumartin, **de Montille**, **Marquis d'Angerville**, **Michel Lafarge** and Roblet-Monnot.

Monthelie (red and white) **Annick Parent** and Denis Boussey.

Auxey-Duresses (red and white) **Claude Maréchal** and Jean-Pierre Diconne.

St-Romain (mainly white) d'Auvenay and Christophe Buisson.

Meursault (white) **des Comtes Lafon £**, **Henri Germain**, **Jean-François Coche-Dury £**, Jean-Michel Gaunoux, **Jean-Philippe Fichet**, Marc Rougeot, Michel Tessier, **Patrick Javillier**, **Roulot** and **Vincent Bouzereau**.

Puligny-Montrachet (white) **Domaine Leflaive £**, **Etienne Sauzet £**, **Louis Carillon**, Olivier Leflaive and Paul Pernot.

Chassagne-Montrachet (white) **Bernard Morey**, Blain-Gagnard, Fontaine-Gagnard, Gagnard-Delagrange, Guy Amiot, Jean-Noël Gagnard, Marc Colin, **Marc Morey**, **Michel Colin-Deléger**, **Michel Niellon** and **Ramonet £**.

St-Aubin (red and white) Gérard Thomas, Henri Prudhon and Hubert & Olivier Lamy.

Santenay (red and white) Vincent Girardin.

CÔTE CHALONNAISE

Rully (red and white) Eric de Suremain, de la Folie, Paul & Henri Jacquesson and Vincent Dureuil-Janthial.

Montagny (white) Stéphane Aladame.

Mercurey (red and white) Antonin Rodet, **Bruno Lorenzon**, Luc Brintet, Michel & Laurent Juillot and J. & F. Raquillet.

Givry (red and white) François Lumpp and Joblot.

MÂCONNAIS

Mâcon, **Pouilly-Fuissé**, **St-Véran** and **Viré-Clessé** (mainly

white) **André Bonhomme**, **Château de Beauregard**,
Château Fuissé (Jean-Jacques Vincent), Daniel Barraud,
des Deux Roches, Goyard, Guillemot-Michel, **Héritiers du
Comte Lafon**, **Jeandeau**, Jean Thévenet, la Croix Senaillet,
la Sarazinière, **Michel Forest**, Robert-Denogent, Talmard
and Verget (Guffens-Heynen).

BEAUJOLAIS
Producing mainly red, the most highly regarded sub-regions
are the ten Cru Villages: **Brouilly**, **Chénas**, **Chiroubles**,
Côte de Brouilly, **Fleurie**, **Juliénas**, **Morgon**, **Moulin-à-Vent**,
Régnié and **St-Amour**.

The top producers are – **Alain Passot**, André Cologne,
Aucoeur, Bernard Mélinand, **F & J Calot**, Champagnon,
Château de Pierreux, **Coudert**, Georges Duboeuf
(domaine-bottled wines only), J.-L. Dutraive, J.-F. Echallier
(des Pins), Hélène & Denis Barbelet, Henry Fessy, Jacky
Janodet, **Jean-Charles Pivot**, **Jean Foillard**, **Louis Jadot
(Château des Jacques)**, Marcel Lapierre, Maurice Gaget,
Michel Chignard, Pascal Granger, Patrick Brunet, **Paul Janin**
and **Vissoux**.

CHAMPAGNE
Each year I try not to list too many non-vintage Champagnes
in my Top 250 because they tend to vary so much in flavour
– bottle age and storage conditions make such a difference.
So the idea with this section of the guide is to use it as a
pointer to the best makers of consistently excellent NV and
vintage Champagne. I have also included a stunning list of
smaller Champagne houses for you to track down when you
are on holiday in France or if you are eagle-eyed and find
them in the UK. These are all terrific estates whose wines
rival the big boys in every department except for price tag.

Billecart-Salmon *NV* Brut Réserve, Brut Rosé, Blanc de Blancs and Demi-Sec. *Vintage* Blanc de Blancs, Le Clos Saint-Hilaire, Cuvée Nicolas-François Billecart, Elisabeth Salmon Rosé and Grande Cuvée.

Bollinger *NV* Special Cuvée. *Vintage* Grande Année, RD and Vieilles Vignes Françaises Blanc de Noirs.

Deutz *Vintage* Blanc de Blancs and Cuvée William Deutz.

Gosset *NV* Brut Excellence, Grande Réserve Brut and Grand Réserve Rosé. *Vintage* Célébris and Grande Millésime Brut.

Alfred Gratien *Vintage* Brut.

Charles Heidsieck *NV* Mise en Cave and Rosé. *Vintage* Brut Millésime.

Jacquesson *Vintage* Avize Grand Cru Blanc de Blancs, Dégorgement Tardive and Grand Vin Signature.

Krug £ *NV* Grande Cuvée. *Vintage* Vintage and Clos du Mesnil.

Laurent-Perrier *NV* Cuvée Rosé Brut, Grand Siècle 'La Cuvée' and Ultra Brut.

Moët & Chandon *Vintage* Brut Impérial and Cuvée Dom Pérignon Brut.

Pol Roger *NV* Brut 'White Foil'. *Vintage* Brut Chardonnay, Brut Rosé, Brut Vintage and Cuvée Sir Winston Churchill.

Louis Roederer *NV* Brut Premier. Vintage Blanc de Blancs, Brut Millésime, Brut Rosé, Cristal and Cristal Rosé.

Ruinart *Vintage* Dom Ruinart Blanc de Blancs and 'R' de Ruinart Brut.

Salon £ *Vintage* Blanc de Blancs.

Taittinger *NV* Brut Réserve and Prélude. *Vintage* Comtes de Champagne Blanc de Blancs.

Alain Thiénot *Vintage* Brut and Grande Cuvée.

Veuve Clicquot *NV* Brut 'Yellow Label' and Demi-Sec. *Vintage* La Grande Dame Brut, La Grande Dame Rosé and Vintage Réserve.

Albert Beerens, André Jacquart, Bertrand Robert, Château de Boursault, Claude Carré, Delamotte, J. Dumangin, Edouard Brun, Egly-Ouriet, Fernand Thill, Fleury, Gatinois, Gérard Dubois, J-M Gobillard, D. Henriet-Bazin, Jacques Selosse, Larmandier-Bernier, Leclerc Briant, Legras, A. Margaine, Le Mesnil, Paul Déthune, Pertois-Moriset, Pierre Gimonnet, Pierre Moncuit, Pierre Vaudon, Roger Brun, G. Tribaut and Vilmart.

ALSACE
Alsace continues its run of wonderful vintages and you really should be making it your mission to search out examples of these wonderful wines. In general, they are under-priced, over-performing, food friendly, aromatic white beauties. From apéritif-style palate soothers, to mid-weight haute cuisine matching styles, to decadently sweet pud wines, this region covers a lot of ground. You will have to look to the smaller, independent wine merchants for most of these names, as they are all fairly small producers. The main grape varieties to seek out are Gewürztraminer, Riesling, Tokay-Pinot Gris, Muscat, Pinot Blanc and Sylvaner. I wouldn't bother with reds and fizzies!

The best producers are – Albert Boxler, Albert Mann, **André Thomas**, Bott-Geyl, Ernest Burn, **Hugel**, **Josmeyer**, Marc Kreydenweiss, **Marcel Deiss**, Mittnacht-Klack, **Ostertag**, Paul Blanck, Rolly Gassmann, Schlumberger, Schoffit, **Trimbach**, **Weinbach** and **Zind-Humbrecht**.

THE LOIRE VALLEY
This rather fragmented list of wines follows the Loire river inland from the Atlantic, picking out the greatest estates from the key areas in this elongated, inexpensive,

yet essential wine region. Sauvignon Blanc and Chenin Blanc are the main white grapes grown here. The Sauvignons are nearly always dry, whereas the Chenins can be fizzy, dry, medium-sweet or full-on sweeties. The majority of serious reds are made from Cabernet Franc, with Gamay and Pinot Noir stepping in for lighter styles.

Muscadet (white) Château de Chasseloir, Chéreau, Luc Choblet, de la Mortaine and **de la Quilla**.

Savennières (white) **des Baumard**, **Clos de la Coulée de Serrant** and La Roche-aux-Moines.

Coteaux du Layon, Coteaux de l'Aubance, Bonnezeaux and **Quarts de Chaume** (white sweeties) **des Baumard**, Château de Fesles, **Château Pierre-Bise**, Didier Richou, Moulin Touchais, de la Roulerie and Vincent Lecointre.

Saumur (sparkling) Bouvet-Ladubay.

Saumur and **Saumur Champigny** (red and white) **du Hureau**, **Filliatreau**, Langlois-Château and **Nerleux**.

Chinon (mainly red) **Philippe Alliet**, **Bernard Baudry**, **Charles Joguet**, Couly-Dutheil and **Desbourdes**.

St-Nicolas de Bourgueil (red) Jean-Paul Mabileau and Max & Lydie Cognard-Taluau.

Bourgueil (red) Joël Taluau, Lamé-Delille-Boucard, **de la Lande (Delaunay)** and **Pierre-Jacques Druet**.

Vouvray (white) Bourillon-Dorléans, **Gaston Huet**, Philippe Foreau and Vincent Rimbault.

Sauvignon de Touraine (white) **Alain Marcadet**.

Gamay de Touraine (red) Henry Marionnet.

Jasnières (white) Jean-Baptiste Pinon and Joël Gigou.

Cheverny (white) de la Gaudronnière and Salvard.

Sancerre (white, rosé and red) Alain Gueneau, **Alphonse Mellot**, André Dézat, **André Vatan**, Bailly-Reverdy, Christian Lauverjat, **Cotat**, **Daulny**, **Henri Bourgeois**, Henri Natter, Merlin-Cherrier, **Pascal & Nicolas Reverdy**,

Philippe de Benoist, **Serge Laloue**, **Sylvain Bailly**, Vacheron and **Vincent Delaporte**.

Pouilly-Fumé (white) André Dézat (Domaine Thibault), **Cédrick Bardin**, **Château du Nozet (de Ladoucette)**, **Château de Tracy**, **Didier Dagueneau**, Hervé Seguin, Jean-Claude Chatelain, **Michel Redde**, Serge Dagueneau and Tabordet.

Menetou-Salon (mainly white) de Chatenoy, **Henry Pellé** and **Jean Teiller**.

Quincy (white) **Jacques Rouzé**.

THE RHÔNE VALLEY

The Rhône Valley is home to a cornucopia of great French wines. It makes some of the most spectacular reds and beguiling whites on the planet, while at the same time giving us amazing bargains and everyday gluggers. It is here that Syrah, Grenache and Mourvèdre rule the reds. Viognier commands the whites in the north, while Roussanne and Marsanne are in charge in the south. If you take the time to get to know this region well, you can drink smartypants wine for very little expenditure.

THE NORTHERN RHÔNE
FROM NORTH TO SOUTH

Côte Rôtie (red) Bernard Burgaud, Chapoutier, **Clusel-Roch £**, **E. Guigal (and Château d'Ampuis) £**, Guy Bernard, **Jamet**, Jean-Michel Gerin, Marius Gentaz-Dervieux, **Pierre Gaillard**, René Rostaing, Yves Cuilleron and **Yves Gangloff £**.

Condrieu (white) **André Perret**, Christian Facchin, **François Villard £**, Georges Vernay, Louis Cheze, Robert Niero and **Yves Cuilleron £**.

St-Joseph (red and white) Bernard Faurie, Delas, **Jean-Louis Chave**, Jean-Louis Grippat and **Pierre Gonon**.

Hermitage (red and white) **Chapoutier £**, Delas, Grippat,

Jean-Louis Chave £, Michel Ferraton, **Paul Jaboulet Ainé £**, Sorrel and **Tardieu-Laurent £**.

Crozes-Hermitage (mainly red) **Alain Graillot**, Albert Belle, du Colombier, Domaine Pochon, **Gilles Robin** and Olivier Dumaine.

Cornas (red) **Alain Voge**, **Auguste Clape**, Jean Lionnet, Noël Verset, **Robert Michel**, **Thierry Allemand** and **du Tunnel** (Stéphane Robert).

THE SOUTHERN RHÔNE

Côtes-du-Rhône and **-Villages** (red) **Brusset**, Château du Trignon, **Clos Petite Bellane**, **Coudoulet de Beaucastel**, Domaine Gramenon, E. Guigal, Marcel Richaud, Piaugier, Rayas (Fonsalette) and **Tardieu-Laurent**.

Lirac, Rasteau, Tavel and **Vacqueyras** (red) **Château des Tours**, Clos des Cazaux, des Espiers, de la Mordorée, **La Soumade** and **du Trapadis**.

Gigondas (red) Château du Trignon, Font-Sane, R. & J.-P. Meffre (Saint-Gayan), **Saint-Cosme** and Santa-Duc.

Châteauneuf-du-Pape (red and white) **de Beaucastel**, Les Cailloux, Chapoutier, de la Charbonnière, **Charvin**, **Clos du Caillou**, **Clos des Papes**, **de Ferrand**, Fortia, **de la Janasse**, de Marcoux, **de la Mordorée**, du Pegaü, **Rayas**, Versino and Le Vieux Donjon.

Muscat de Beaumes-de-Venise (sweet white) Chapoutier, **Domaine de Durban** and Paul Jaboulet Ainé.

FRENCH COUNTRY

This may be the most dishevelled section in this chapter (Italy is a close second), but if you take it slowly you'll find some amazing, handcrafted wines here, that don't cost a bomb and deliver amazing amounts of flavour. 'French Country' is an old-fashioned term that really just means 'the rest of France's wine regions'. Years ago this would be a jumbled mass of funky, artisan estates, some of which made passable wines, and others that bumbled along selling their bottles to their friends and local restaurants. How things have changed! There is nothing other than exceptionally professional, totally committed producers, world-class expertise in this list, making some of the most remarkable and unique wine in the whole of France.

SOUTHWEST FRANCE

Bergerac (red and white) de la Jaubertie, **Moulin des Dames** and **La Tour des Gendres**.

Cahors (reds) **du Cèdre**, **Clos Triguedina**, Lagrezette and **Les Laquets**.

Jurançon (dry and sweet whites) Bellegarde, **Cauhapé**, **Charles Hours**, Clos Guirouilh, **Clos Lapeyre**, Clos Uroulat and de Lahargue.

Madiran (reds) d'Aydie, **Alain Brumont (Bouscassé and Montus)** and Domaine Pichard.

Monbazillac (sweet white) de l'Ancienne Cure, la Borderie and **Tirecul La Gravière**.

Saussignac (sweet white) Château Richard and Clos d'Yvigne.

LANGUEDOC-ROUSSILLON

Banyuls (fortified) and **Collioure** (red) de la Casa Blanca, Château de Jau, **du Mas Blanc** and de la Rectoire.

La Clape (red and white) **Camplazens**, **Château de Capitoul**, **de l'Hospitalet**, de la Negly and Pech-Redon.

Corbières (mainly red) **La Baronne**, des Chandelles, Château les Palais, Château Vaugélas, Etang des Colombes, **de Lastours**, **Meunier St Louis** and **Pech-Latt**.

Costières de Nîmes (red, white and rosé) des Aveylans, de Belle-Coste, Grande-Cassagne, Mourgues-du-Grès and **de Nages**.

Coteaux du Languedoc (red and white) Abbaye de

Valmagne, **d'Aupilhac**, Les Aurelles, **Mas d'Azelon**, Mas de Chimères, Font Caude, Mas Jullien, **Mas Mortiès**, Peyre Rose, Puech-Haut, **Roc d'Anglade** and La Sauvagéonne.

Faugères (mainly red) **Alquier**, **de Ciffre** and des **Estanilles**.

Minervois (red and white) **Borie de Maurel**, **Le Cazal**, **Clos Centeilles**, Fabas, de Gourgazaud, **Lignon** and d'Oupia.

Pic St-Loup (mainly red) Cazeneuve, Ermitage du Pic St-Loup, **de l'Hortus**, **de Lascaux**, Lascours and Mas Bruguière.

St-Chinian (red and white) **Canet-Valette**, **Cazal-Viel**, Coujan, des Jougla and Mas Champart.

Miscellaneous estates of excellence (and where to find them): **de l'Aigle** – Limoux; **Bégude** – Limoux; **Cazes** – Rivesaltes; **Clos des Fées** – Côtes de Roussillon-Villages; **Domaine de Baruel** – Cévennes; **Domaine Gardiés** – Côtes de Roussillon-Villages; **Domaine des Ravanès** – Coteaux de Murveil; **Elian da Ros** – Côtes du Marmandais; **de la Granges des Pères** – l'Hérault; **Mas Amiel** – Maury; **Mas de Daumas Gassac** – l'Hérault.

PROVENCE

Bandol (red) **de la Bégude**, Château Jean-Pierre Gaussen, **Lafran-Veyrolles**, La Laidière, Mas de la Rouvière, Maubernard, de Pibarnon, **Pradeaux**, **Ray-Jane**, Souviou, **La Suffrène** and **Tempier**.

Les Baux-de-Provence (mainly red) Hauvette, des Terres Blanches and **de Trévallon £**.

Bellet (red, white and rosé) Château de Crémat.

Cassis (mainly white) Clos Ste-Madeleine.

Côtes de Provence (mainly red) **de la Courtade**, Gavoty, de Rimauresq and de St-Baillon.

Palette (red, white and rosé) **Château Simone**.

GERMANY

Germany is making better wines than ever before. You must start drinking them, if you haven't already re-ignited your enthusiasm, because the exceptional Rieslings that hail from these historic vineyards are life changing. German Riesling is a fundamental cornerstone of everyone's wine diet. The new, drier styles of Riesling are simply spellbinding. The long-awaited Riesling revolution is here – join in! What follows is the hit list of some of the finest exponents of this grape variety on the planet. All you have to do is find them and drink them. Independent merchants will help in this quest.

The best producers are – Balthasar Ress, **J.B. Becker**, Dr Bürklin-Wolf, J.J. Cristoffel, Daniel Vollenweider, Dönnhoff, **Egon Müller**, Heymann-Löwenstein, **Fritz Haag**, Koehler-Ruprecht, Künstler, J.L. Wolf, **Josef Leitz**, **Freiherr Langwerth von Simmern**, H. & R. Lingenfelder, **Dr. Loosen**, Müller-Cattoir, **J.J. Prüm**, **Reichsgraf von Kesselstatt**, **Max Ferd**, **Richter**, Reichsrat von Buhl, Reinhold Haart, **Robert Weil**, Schloss Lieser, Schloss Reinhartshausen, **Selbach-Oster**, **von Schubert-Maximin Grünhaus**, **St. Urbans-Hof**, **Dr. H. Thanisch Erben**, Weingut Kerpen, **Weingut Karthäuserhof** and Willi Schaefer.

GREAT BRITAIN

After the last few balmy summers, global warming is definitely on England's side when it comes to winemaking. If you believe the papers, then even the French are looking to invest in sparkling wine operations in the south of England! Sparklers and dry whites are where you should be spending your money. It is a shame, though, that we still have to pay duty to the government on our purchases of English wine. If you took £2 or so off every bottle of English wine on the shelves, it might encourage us to make more and better wines, at the expense of boring Cava from Spain, and lacklustre dry whites from Germany or the Loire. Now there's a thought! Lobby your local MP please. Remember prices are lowest if you buy direct and also almost all UK wineries welcome visitors – see www.englishwineproducers.com.

The chosen few are – Biddenden, **Camel Valley**, **Chapel Down (Curious Grape)**, Clay Hill, Coddington, **Davenport**, Nyetimber, RidgeView and Shawsgate.

ITALY

Italy is home to the most ridiculously disorganised wine industry, hundreds of obscure, indigenous grape varieties and many thousands of different bottles of wine. But, despite being frighteningly complicated, I have still managed to bring some semblance of order to this entry! This is a bang-up-to-date list of the best Italian producers available in the UK. Italy makes some of the finest value wines on the shelves, and if you are tempted to venture up the price ladder, you'll find they also make seriously brilliant wines around the £10 to £15 pound mark, too. But, like most of my serious wines, you will probably have to go to top-quality independent wine merchants to find the majority of the estates listed below.

NORTHWEST
PIEDMONT
Barolo, Barbaresco, Barbera, Dolcetto and other reds – Aldo Conterno, Angelo Gaja £, Ascheri, Bruno

Rocca, Ca' Rossa, Ceretto, Cigliuti, Conterno Fantino, Domenico Clerico, **Elio Altare**, **Fontanafredda**, Giacomo Conterno, Giuseppe Mascarello, **Luciano Sandrone**, **Paolo Scavino**, **Parusso**, E. Pira, **Roberto Voerzio** and **La Spinetta**.

Moscato (fizzy, sweet white) **Fontanafredda** and **La Spinetta**.

Gavi (dry white) **La Giustiniana**, Nicola Bergaglio and **La Scolca**.

Roero Arneis (red and dry white) **Bric Cenciurio**, **Matteo Correggia** and Carlo Deltetto.

LOMBARDY

Red and white – **Bellavista** (Franciacorta), **Ca' del Bosco** (Franciacorta), **Ca' dei Frati** (Lugana), **Fratelli Muratori** (Franciacorta) and **Nino Negri** (Valtellina).

NORTHEAST

TRENTINO

All styles – Bossi Fedrigotti, Endrizzi, **Ferrari**, **Foradori**, Letrari, Pojer & Sandri, **San Leonardo**, Vigneto Dalzocchio and **La-Vis**.

ALTO ADIGE

All styles – Alois Lageder, **Colterenzio**, **Franz Haas**, Hofstätter and **San Michele Appiano**.

VENETO

Soave (white) Ca' Rugate, Gini, **Pieropan**, Prà and **Roberto Anselmi**.

Valpolicella (red) **Allegrini**, Ca' del Pipa, Dal Forno, **Giuseppe Quintarelli** £ and Masi.

Miscellaneous estates of excellence – (fizz) **Ruggeri** (Valdobbiadene); (reds and sweeties) **Maculan** (Breganze).

FRIULI-VENEZIA GIULIA

Mainly white – **Dario Raccaro**, Davide Moschioni, **Giovanni Puiatti**, Girolamo Dorigo, **Lis Neris (Alvararo Pecorari)**,

Livio Felluga, Mario Schiopetto, Miani, Ronco del Gnemiz, Roncùs, Tercic, Villa Russiz and Vinnaioli Jermann.

CENTRAL
TUSCANY
Chianti (red) P. Antinori, Carobbio, Castello di Brolio, Castello di Fonterutoli, Felsina Berardenga, Le Filigare, Fontodi, Isole e Olena, La Massa, Il Molino di Grace, Poggerino, Querciabella, Selvapiana and Villa Caffagio.
Brunello di Montalcino (red) Altesino, Argiano, Case Basse, Ciacci Piccolomini d'Aragona, Collosorbo, Corte Pavone, Costanti, Donatella Cinelli Colombini, Fanti San Filippo, Fuligni, La Gerla, Lisini, Mastrojanni, Pietroso, Poggio Antico, Il Poggione, Sesti, Silvio Nardi and Uccelliera.
Vino Nobile di Montepulciano (red) Dei, Il Macchione, Poliziano and Villa Sant'Anna.
Carmignano (red) Ambra and Tenuta di Capezzana.
Super-Tuscans (red) Il Borro, Il Bosco (Manzano), Brancaia, Camartina (Querciabella) £, Campora (Falchini), Il Carbonaione (Poggio Scalette), Casalfero (Barone Ricasoli), Cepparello (Isole e Olena) £, Cortaccio (Villa Caffagio), Flaccianello della Pieve (Fontodi), Fontalloro (Felsina Berardenga), Ghiaie della Furba (Capezzana), Lupicaia (Tenuta del Terricio) £, Masseto (L. Antinori), Nambrot (Tenuta di Ghizzano) £, Ornellaia (Mondavi/L. Antinori) £, Palazzo Altesi (Altesino), Paleo Rosso (Le Macchiole), Le Pergole Torte (Montevertine), Saffredi (Le Pupille) £, Sammarco (Castello dei Rampolla), Sassicaia (Marchesi Incisa della Rochetta) £, Siepi (Fonterutoli) £, Solaia (P. Antinori) £, Solengo (Argiano) £, Tassinaia (Tenuta del Terriccio) and Tignanello (P. Antinori).
Maremma and Morellino (mainly red) Costanza Malfatti, Lohsa (Poliziano), Le Pupille and Tenuta di Belguardo & Poggio Bronzone (Mazzei).

Vernaccia di San Gimignano (white) Montenidoli, **Panizzi**, Pietraserena and Teruzzi & Puthod.

Vin Santo (sweetie) **Avignonesi £**, **Isole e Olena £**, Selvapiana and Villa Branca.

MARCHE

Red and white – **Coroncino**, Saladini Pilastri, **Le Terrazze** and **Umani Ronchi**.

UMBRIA

Red and white – **Arnaldo Caprai**, La Carraia, **Castello della Sala**, **La Fiorita Lamborghini**, Luigi Bigi, **Lungarotti**, **Palazzone** and **Sportoletti**.

LAZIO

Red and white – **Castel De Paolis**, **Falesco** and Pallavincini.

ABRUZZO AND MOLISE

Red and white – **Edoardo Valentini**, **Di Majo Norante**, Podere Castorani and Valle Reale.

SOUTHERN AND ISLANDS – (ALL STYLES)

PUGLIA

Angelo Rocca, Apollonio, Botromagno, **Cosimo Taurino**, Francesco Candido, **Tenuta Rubino** and Vallone.

CAMPANIA

Colli di Lapio, Feudi di San Gregorio, **Luigi Maffini**, **Mastroberardino**, **Montevetrano** and **Taburno**.

BASILICATA

D'Angelo, Basilisco and Paternoster.

CALABRIA

Librandi and San Francesco.

SICILY AND PANTELLERIA

Abbazia Santa Anastasia, **Abraxas**, De Bartoli, Cusumano, Inycon, **Maurigi**, **Morgante**, **Planeta**, Salvatore Murana and Tasca d'Almerita.

SARDINIA

Argiolas, **Gallura**, Giovanni Cherchi, **Santadi** and Sella & Mosca.

NEW ZEALAND

I truly believe that New Zealand has turned a corner of sorts. Last year, at the Air New Zealand Awards (at which I was a judge), all but one of the Trophy winning wines was sealed with a screwcap – and yes, that included all of the reds! Only a fizzy had a Champagne-style cork in it. Add this daring, and yet wholly defensible move (screwcaps are the only way forward in my opinion to guarantee your wine is in perfect nick) to the fact that I had never tasted such a remarkable array of Kiwi wine in my life. Things are looking up! More estates' wines are available in the UK than ever before. Sauvignon Blanc has always been the main appeal for punters, but Pinot Noir is looking good, too, and don't forget about Chardonnays, Rieslings (and other aromatics) and even Cabernets, Merlots and Syrahs, now that Hawke's Bay has got its collective eye zeroed in on the target.

It has been painful waiting for this to happen. I like a healthy bit of sport on wine shop shelves and it seems that New Zealand finally wants to join in with the rest of the world.

What follows is the most up-to-date list of NZ wines I have ever published! Read it carefully and then relax into some truly brilliant wines.

The best estates – Alana Estate, Allan Scott, Alpha Domus, Amisfield, Astrolabe, **Ata Rangi**, **Blind River**, Borthwick, Cable Bay, **Carrick**, Chard Farm, **Cloudy Bay**, **Craggy Range**, The Crossings, **Dog Point**, **Dry River**, Esk Valley, **Felton Road**, **Forrest Estate**, Foxes Island, Framingham, Goldwater Estate, Grove Mill, Hawkesbridge, Highfield, **Huia**, **Hunter's**, **Isabel Estate**, **Jackson Estate**, Kathy Lynskey, Kim Crawford, **Kumeu River**, Lawson's Dry Hills, **Martinborough Vineyards**, Matahiwi, **Matakana Estate**,

Mills Reef, **Mt Difficulty**, Mount Edward, Mount Michael, **Mountford**, Mud House, **Murdoch James**, **Ngatarawa**, Olssens, **Palliser Estate**, Passage Rock, **Pegasus Bay**, **Peregrine**, Pisa Range, Rippon, Rockburn, Sacred Hill, **Saint Clair**, **Seresin**, Sileni, Sleeping Dogs, Solstone, Spy Valley, **Stonecroft**, **Stonyridge**, Te Mata, **TerraVin**, Te Whare Ra, Trinity Hill, Tohu, **Two Paddocks**, **Unison**, Valli, **Vavasour**, **Vidal**, **Villa Maria**, Wairau River, West Brook and **Wither Hills**.

PORTUGAL

Portugal will always make two of the finest fortified wines in the world – port and Madeira. These two tremendous creations are staggeringly serious in the right hands. Unfortunately they suffer from being a little out of fashion. Buck the trend and discover just how wonderful these wines are. I have the definitive list of top producers for you here. In addition to this, I have also compiled a list of the top producers of non-fortified wines. I must admit that I don't drink much Portuguese wine at home, but things are moving forward smoothly and the future is bright. This is the year I make an effort with Portugal.

PORT
The best special-occasion port houses are – **Dow**, **Fonseca**, **Graham**, **Quinta do Noval Nacional**, **Taylor** and **Warre**. The less famous overachievers are – Churchill, **Niepoort**, **Quinta do Portal**, **Quinta do Vesuvio**, Quinto do Infantado, Ramos-Pinto and **Senhora da Ribeira**.

MADEIRA
The top producers are – **Blandy's**, **Cossart Gordon** and **Henriques & Henriques**.

THE REST OF PORTUGAL

Here's a short hit list of fine winemakers in the better regions.

Alentejo Cortes de Cima, Quinta de Cabriz, Quinta do Carmo, **João Portugal Ramos** and Segada.

Bairrada Caves São João and **Luis Pato**.

Beiras Caves Aliança.

Dão Alvaro Castro, Conde de Santar, Quinta da Cabriz, Quinta dos Carvalhais and **Quinta dos Roques**.

Douro Duas Quintas, **Niepoort**, **Quinta do Crasto**, Quinta da Gaivosa, Quinta do Infantado, **Quinta do Portal**, Quinta de Roriz, Quinta de la Rosa, Quinta do Vale da Raposa and Redoma.

Estremadura Palha Canas, **Quinta da Boavista** and Quinta de Pancas.

Ribatejo Bright Brothers and **Quinta da Lagoalva**.

Terras do Sado João Pires, **José-Maria da Fonseca**, Pasmados, Periquita and **Quinta de Camarate**.

Vinho Verde Palácio da Brejoeira and **Quinta do Ameal**.

SOUTH AFRICA

South Africa's march forward continues apace. It is amazing to think that in the space of only a decade or so, this archaic industry has reinvented itself and come out fighting. I am off to South Africa again next year for another mammoth tour and I expect to add even more estates to this exponentially growing list. Sauvignon, Chenin Blanc and Chardonnay are the white grapes to watch, and I suspect that Syrah and clever Rhône blends will end up being the strong suit with regard to reds. But don't forget the Cabernets, Merlots and Cape blends, which utilise local favourite Pinotage to its best effect. South Africa has arrived with a bang on the world market and it is here to stay.

The top producers are – Avondale, Beyerskloof, **Boekenhoutskloof (Porcupine Ridge)**, **Bouchard Finlayson**, **Brahms**, Coleraine, **Columella (Sadie Family)**, **De Toren**, De Trafford, De Wetshof, **Diemersfontein**, **Dornier (Donatus in the UK)**, **Fairview**, **Flagstone**, **Glen Carlou**, Graham Beck, Grangehurst, **Hamilton Russell**, Hartenberg, **Iona**, **Jean Daneel**, **Jordan**, Kanonkop, **Ken Forrester**, Klein Constantia, **Lammershoek**, Land's End, Lindhorst, Linton Park, Longridge, **Luddite**, **Meinert**, Mischa, Mont Rochelle, **Mont du Toit**, Morgenhof, La Motte, Neil Ellis, Nelson's Creek, Newton Johnson, L'Ormarins, Paul Cluver, **Phileo**, **Raats**, Remhoogte, **Rijk's**, Rudera, Rupert & Rothschild, **Rustenberg (Brampton)**, Rust en Vrede, **Scali**, Signal Hill, Simonsig, Southern Right, Spice Route, **Springfield**, Stark-Condé, Stellenzicht, Thelema, Veenwouden, **Vergelegen**, **Vilafonte**, Viljoensdrift, Villiera, **Warwick Estate**, **Waterford (Kevin Arnold)** and Wildekrans.

SPAIN

I have listed my Spanish wines by region first and then by producer. Spain is still woefully under represented in the UK at the top end but, bit by bit, Spanish companies are encouraging us to understand and accept their new wines. There is so much development and modernisation going on that I think, in the next ten years, it will become a real force to be reckoned with worldwide.

ANDALUCÍA
Jerez (sherry) **Emilio Lustau**, **Fernando de Castilla**, **González Byass**, Hidalgo, Osborne and **Valdespino**.

ARAGÓN
Calatayud Marqués de Aragón and San Gregorio.

Campo de Borja Bodegas Borsao.
Somontano Blecua (Viñas del Vero) and Enate.

CASTILLA Y LEÓN
Bierzo Descendientes de J. Palacios.
Ribera del Duero Alión, Cillar de Silos, Condado de Haza,
Dominio de Pingus, Pago de Carraovejas, Pesquera, Tarsus,
Valduero and Vega Sicilia £.
Valladolid Mauro.
Rueda Agrícola Castellana and Bodegas Dos Victorias.
Toro Alquiriz (Vega Sicilia) and Viña Bajoz.
Arribes del Duero Durius Alto Duero (Marqués de
Griñon).

CATALUÑA
Conca de Barberá Josep Foraster and Miguel Torres.
Empordà-Costa Brava Mas Estela.
Penedès Albet I Noya, Can Ràfols dels Caus, Jean Léon,
Marquès de Monistrol, Miguel Torres and Puig i Roca.
Tarragona-Montsant and Priorat Celler de Capçanes,
Clos Mogador £, Clos de L'Obac, Dits Del Terra,
L'Ermita and Finca Dofi (Alvaro Palacios), Laurona,
Mas d'en Compte, Mas Igneus, Mas Martinet and
Scala Dei.
Terra Alta Bàrbara Forés and Xavier Clua.

EXTREMADURA, CASTILLA-LA MANCHA AND MADRID
Almansa Piqueras.
Castilla-La Mancha Dominio de Valdepusa.
Valdepeñas Los Llanos.

ISLANDS
Mallorca Anima Negra.

LEVANTE
Jumilla Casa de la Ermita.
Valencia Dominio Los Pinos.

NORTHERN COASTAL SPAIN
Rías Baixas Fillaboa, **Lagar de Cervera**, Lagar de Fornelos, Martín Codax, **Pazo de Barrantes**, **Pazo Señoráns**, Valdamor and Valmiñor.
Bizkaiko and Getariako Txacolina Bodegas Ametzoi and **Txomín Etaniz**.

RIOJA AND NAVARRA
Rioja Artadi, Barón de Ley, **Contino**, **CVNE**, Lopez de Heredia, **Marqués de la Concordia**, **Marqués de Griñon**, **Marqués de Murrieta**, **Marqués de Vargas**, Muga.
Navajas Remelluri, La Rioja Alta, **Roda**, Urbina and Viña Salceda.
Navarra Agramont, Guelbenzu, Julián Chivite, Ochoa, Príncipe de Viana and **Vega del Castillo**.

USA
CALIFORNIA
While there is still a band of ridiculously narcissistic micro-boutiques flogging their wine to like-minded mugs at astronomical prices, the majority of winemakers in the USA look at the world with level heads. This means there are plenty of wines for us to choose from at reasonable prices. The main problem is that this huge industry has no trouble in selling its wines locally and so they are understandably lazy about their export markets. Comparing like for like in the New World arena, California has many wines to be proud of, but value for money is still an issue. New Zealand

(with Pinot Noir), Australia (with Cabernet, Shiraz/Syrah and Chardonnay) and South America (with Bordeaux blends) are the countries that take chunks out of it at the £10 mark, but as you drift upwards, California has some real gems worth tracking down. Also, whenever you need a hit of Zinfandel (and we all do from time to time), this is the place to come.

I have arranged the wineries in order of wine style, rather than by region, as most producers source grapes from far and wide, and it is also easier for me to get my head around!

Cabernet Sauvignon/Merlot/Cabernet Franc Araujo, **Arietta £**, Beringer, **Bryant Family £**, Cain, **Caymus £**, Clos LaChance, **Corison**, **Dalle Valle £**, **Diamond Creek £**, Dominus, **Duckhorn**, Dunn, **Etude**, Flora Springs, **Forman**, **Frog's Leap**, Gallo Estate, **Harlan Estate £**, Havens, Hess Collection, **Joseph Phelps £**, Justin Vineyards, Lail Vineyards, Matanzas Creek, **Moraga**, **Niebaum Coppola**, **Newton £**, **Opus One**, Pahlmeyer, **Paradigm £**, Paul Hobbs, **Peter Michael £**, Philip Togni, **Quintessa £**, **Ridge £**, Robert Mondavi, St Francis, **Shafer £**, Silver Oak, **Spottswoode £**, **Stag's Leap Wine Cellars £** and **Viader £**.

Chardonnay Arrowood, **Au Bon Climat**, Beringer, Clos LaChance, **David Ramey**, **Frog's Leap**, Gallo Estate, **Hanzell £**, **Kistler £**, **Kongsgaard £**, **Landmark £**, **Lymar £**, Morgan, Paul Hobbs, **Peter Michael £**, **Shafer £** and Sinskey.

Sauvignon Blanc Beringer, Carmenet, **Frog's Leap**, Matanzas Creek and **Robert Mondavi**.

Pinot Noir Au Bon Climat, **Calera £**, Cinnabar, **Etude £**, Gary Farrell, **Hanzell**, **Kistler £**, Marimar Torres, **J. Rochioli £**, Saintsbury, Sinskey and Talley Vineyards.

Rhône Rangers Alban, Au Bon Climat, Bonny Doon, **Cline**, Jade Mountain, JC Cellars, **Qupé**, **Sean Thackrey**, Tablas Creek £, **Turley £** and Wild Hog.

Zinfandel Biale, **Cline**, **Elyse**, Dash Cellars, **Doug Nalle**, De Loach, **Ravenswood**, Renwood, **Ridge £**, Rosenblum, **Seghesio** and **Turley £**.
Sparkling Domaine Carneros, **Domaine Chandon**, Mumm Napa, **Roederer Estate** and **Schramsberg**.
Inexpensive estates Avila, Bogle, Concannon, Estancia, **Fetzer Bonterra**, Hahn, Kendall-Jackson, J. Lohr, Marietta Cellars, **Ramsay**, Seventh Moon and Wente.

PACIFIC NORTHWEST
Wines from Oregon and Washington State are still hard to get hold of in the UK and, therefore, are expensive. Good luck with your search – these producers make sensational wines.

Oregon's best estates – **Adelsheim**, Archery Summit, Beaux Frères, Bethel Heights, **Cristom**, **Domaine Drouhin £**, Duck Pond, **Evesham Wood**, King Estate, Ponzi and Rex Hill.
Washington State's best estates – **Andrew Will £**, Château Ste-Michelle, DiStefano, **L'Ecole No 41**, **Leonetti Cellar £**, **Pepper Bridge**, **Quilceda Creek £**, Snoqualmie, **Woodward Canyon** and **Zefina**.

THE REST OF THE WORLD
Once again, in the interests of keeping things relatively sane, I have skipped out a load of less important (in my opinion – I don't mind causing a riot) winemaking countries and regions in the main body of the text, in order to give them a chance to chuck their hat into the ring in this paragraph. I know that the Jura, Savoie and Corsica were missed out of the French section, but I haven't drunk any bottles from any of these regions this year. Not one of the 30,000 wines that passed my lips came from these areas – so how important can they be? While Austria warrants its own mini-listing,

Switzerland's fine wines fail to register on my Richter scale. This might be different if the Swiss didn't drink all of their wine in their own country!

Eastern Europe still leaves me cold, but it has to be said that Nagyréde and Riverview from Hungary are good operations, and, despite the lurid labels and preposterous poster campaign, Blueridge from Bulgaria manages to make passable wine. I don't drink them – if you have a fiver to spend I can give you a load of options in the 250 to spend it on – but loads of people do. Tokaji from Hungary is widely regarded as the greatest wine from Eastern Europe, and if you haven't experienced this incredible burst of honeyed, luxurious, tropical fruit before, you should find a bottle immediately. They are, admittedly, all pretty expensive (around £20 for a 50cl bottle – but they go a long way). Look out for these producers – Disznókö, Oremus and the Royal Tokaji Wine Company.

Château Musar is still the Lebanon's most famous wine and Israel is apparently making some half decent wine, too, but I haven't seen any samples. Greek wines are continuing to improve, with Boutari, Gaia Estate, Gerovassiliou, Kir-Yanni, Nikos Lazaridis, Tsantali and Tselepos my favourite estates. I thankfully have managed to avoid Cypriot wine and the charms of Tenerife's finest. North African wines, from Tunisia and Morocco, are occasionally seen on UK shelves. There are some pretty chunky Carignans around, but nothing that can't be trumped by Sicilian Nero d'Avola or Primitivo from Puglia.

Mexican, Bolivian and Peruvian wines are still a mystery to me (thank goodness), and I have not repeated last year's near fatal brush with Chinese wine. Uruguay is trying hard to excite, but only Filgueria, Juanicó and Preludio, to date, have made swallowable wines. The Hatten winery in Bali is still going strong, as are the Monsoon Valley wines from

Thailand and the fascinating Sula Vineyard projects in India.
Most of these guys are in the UK now and are starting to
try and get on to Indian and Asian restaurant wine lists.
If the quality is up there (and some bottles look OK),
we should be able to drink truly authentic, indigenous
wines with our Asian and Indian cuisine in the near future.
On that cheery note, I will say Cheers!

DIRECTORY
OF UK WINE
MERCHANTS

If your favourite wine shop isn't here, or if you're a brand new wine merchant and want to be included, then drop me a line (address on page 255). Subject to a thorough grilling, I will put you in next year's book!

✪ = Jukesy-rated wine merchant worthy of particular note
C = Wine sold by the case (often mixed) of twelve bottles
M = Mail order company, usually with no retail premises
F = Fine wine sales/wine broker/good range of expensive stuff!

RECOMMENDED LARGER CHAIN STORES AND SUPERMARKETS (PLUS ABBREVIATIONS)

Asda (Asd) 289 stores 0500 100055 www.asda.co.uk ✪

E.H. Booth & Co., of Lancashire, Cheshire, Cumbria and Yorkshire (**Boo**) 26 stores 01772 251701 www.booths-supermarkets.co.uk ✪

Co-operative Group CWS (Coo) 2,000 stores 0800 068 6727 www.co-op.co.uk

Majestic Wine Warehouses (Maj) 122 stores 01923 298200 www.majestic.co.uk ✪C

Marks & Spencer (M&S) over 400 stores 020 7935 4422 www.marksandspencer.com ✪

Wm Morrison (Mor) more than 400 stores 01924 870000 www.morereasons.co.uk

Oddbins (Odd) 227 stores and **Oddbins Fine Wine shops (OFW)** 8 stores 020 8944 4400 www.oddbins.com ✪

Sainsbury's (Sai) 728 stores 0800 636262 www.sainsburys.co.uk ✪

Somerfield Stores (Som) 912 stores 0117 935 6669 www.somerfield.co.uk

Tesco Stores (Tes) 1,878 stores 0800 505555 www.tesco.com ✪

Thresher Group – including **Thresher (Thr)** and **Wine Rack (WRa)** just under 2,000 stores 01707 387200 www.threshergroup.com ✪

Unwins Ltd (**Unw**) 384 stores 01322 272711
www.unwins.co.uk

Waitrose (**Wai**) 147 stores 01344 825232
www.waitrose.com ✪

Wine Cellar (**WCe**) 235 stores 0800 838251
www.winecellar.co.uk

RECOMMENDED INDEPENDENT RETAIL SPECIALISTS, SMALL CHAINS, WINE BROKERS AND MAIL ORDER WINE COMPANIES SORTED ALPHABETICALLY

A & A Wines, Cranleigh, Surrey 01483 274666
aawines@aol.com **C**

A & B Vintners, Brenchley, Kent 01892 724977
info@abvintners.co.uk ✪**MC**

Abbey Wines, Melrose, Roxburghshire 01896 823224

Adnams Wine Merchants, Southwold, Suffolk
01502 727200 wines@adnams.co.uk ✪

Ameys Wines, Sudbury, Suffolk 01787 377144 ✪

Amps Fine Wines of Oundle, near Peterborough,
Northamptonshire 01832 273502
info@ampsfinewines.co.uk

Arkell Vintners, Swindon, Wiltshire 01793 823026
wines@arkells.com

John Armit Wines, London 020 7908 0600
info@armit.co.uk ✪**MCF**

W.J. Armstrong, East Grinstead, West Sussex 01342 321478
www.wjarmstrong.com

Arnolds, Broadway, Worcestershire 01386 852427

Arriba Kettle & Co., Honeybourne,
Worcestershire 01386 833024
arriba.kettle@btopenworld.com **C**

Australian Wine Club, Slough, Berkshire 0800 8562004
orders@australianwine.co.uk ✪**MC**

Averys, Bristol 0117 921 4146 ✪

Bacchanalia, Cambridge 01223 576292 ✪
Bacchus Fine Wines, Warrington, Buckinghamshire
  01234 711140 wine@bacchus.co.uk ✪C
Bakers & Larners, Holt, Norfolk 01263 712323
  ctbaker@cwcom.net
Stanley Ball, Crawley, West Sussex 01293 525777
  stanley_ball@msn.com
Ballantynes, Cowbridge, Vale of Glamorgan 01446 774840
  enq@ballantynes.co.uk ✪
Balls Brothers, London 020 7739 1642
  wine@ballsbrothers.co.uk MC
Georges Barbier, London 020 8852 5801
  georgesbarbier@f2s.com ✪MC
Barrels & Bottles, Sheffield 0114 255 6611
  sales@barrelsandbottles.co.uk
Bat & Bottle, Oakham, Rutland 0845 108 4407
  post@batwine.com ✪
Beaconsfield Wine Cellar, Beaconsfield, Buckinghamshire
01494 675545 thecellars@btinternet.com
Bedales, London 020 7403 8853 info@bedalestreet.com
Bella Wines, Newmarket, Suffolk 01638 604899
  sales@bellawines.co.uk ✪M
Bennetts Fine Wines, Chipping Campden, Gloucestershire
  01386 840392 enquiries@bennettsfinewines.com ✪
Bentalls, Kingston-upon-Thames, Surrey 020 8546 1001
Bergerac Wine Cellar, St Helier, Jersey 01534 870756
Berkmann Wine Cellars, London 020 7609 4711
  info@berkmann.co.uk ✪M
Berry Bros. & Rudd, London 0870 900 4300
  www.bbr.com ✪F
Best Cellars, Ashburton, Devon 01364 652546
  sales@bestcellars.co.uk
Bibendum Wine Ltd, London 020 7449 4120
  sales@bibendum-wine.co.uk ✪MCF

M = Mail order company, usually with no retail premises
F = Fine wine sales/wine broker/good range of expensive stuff!

Bideford Wines, Bideford, Devon 01237 470507
Bintwo, Padstow, Cornwall 01841 532022
 david@bintwo.com ✪
Le Bon Vin, Sheffield 0114 2560090 sales@lebonvin.co.uk
Bonhote Foster, Bumpstead, Suffolk 01440 730779
 info@bonhotefoster.co.uk **M**
Booths of Stockport, Heaton Moor, Stockport
 0161 432 3309 johnbooth@lineone.net
Bordeaux Index, London 020 7253 2110
 sales@bordeauxindex.com ✪**MF**
The Bottleneck, Broadstairs, Kent 01843 861095
 sales@thebottleneck.co.uk
Bowland Forest Vintners, Clitheroe, Lancashire
 01200 448688 milescorish@aol.com
Brinkleys Wines, London 020 7351 1683 www.brinkleys.com
Burgundy Shuttle, London 07771 630826 **MC**
Burgundy Wines, Brighton, East Sussex 01273 330012
 md@BurgundyWines.co.uk
Butlers Wine Cellar, Brighton, East Sussex 01273 698724
 henry@butlers-winecellar.co.uk ✪
Anthony Byrne Fine Wines, Ramsey, Cambridgeshire
 01487 814555 sales@abfw.co.uk **MC**
D. Byrne & Co., Clitheroe, Lancashire 01200 423152 ✪

Cadman Fine Wines, Northampton, Northamptonshire
 0845 1214011 sales@cadmanfinewines.co.uk
Cairns & Hickey, Bramhope, Leeds 0113 267 3746
 pcairns@c-hwines.fsnet.co.uk
Cape Wine & Food, Staines, Middlesex 01784 451860
 capewineandfood@aol.com
Carley & Webb, Framlingham, Suffolk 01728 723503
Carringtons, Manchester 0161 466 2546
Castang Wine Shippers, Pelynt, Cornwall 01503 220359
 sales@castang-wines.co.uk **MC**

Cave Cru Classé, London 020 7378 8579
enquiries@ccc.co.uk **MCF**

Les Caves du Patron, Stoneygate, Leicester 0116 221 8221
wines@lescavesdupatron.com

Les Caves de Pyrene, Guildford, Surrey 01483 538820
sales@lescaves.co.uk ❖

Ceci Paolo, Ledbury, Herefordshire 01531 632976
www.cecipaolo.com

The Cellar Door, Overton, Hampshire 01256 770 397
info@thecellardoor.co.uk

Cellar Door Wines, St Albans, Hertfordshire 01727 854488
sales@cellardoorwines.co.uk

The Champagne & Wine Cellar, Winchcombe,
Gloucestershire 01242 603514
grape.expectations@btinternet.com

Andrew Chapman Fine Wines, Abingdon, Oxfordshire
0845 458 0707 info@surf4wine.co.uk ❖

Simon Charles Vintners, London 020 7228 3409
wine@scvintners.f9.co.uk ❖

The Charterhouse Wine Co., Spalding, Lincolnshire
01775 720 300 info@charterhousewine.co.uk

Cheers Wine Merchants, Swansea 01792 403895
andrewcheers@hotmail.com

Cheshire Smokehouse, Wilmslow, Cheshire 01625 540123
sales@cheshiresmokehouselimited.co.uk

Chiltern Cellars, High Wycombe, Buckinghamshire
01494 526212

Chippendale Fine Wines, Bradford, West Yorkshire
01274 582424 mikepoll@chippendalewine.free-
online.co.uk **MC**

Church House Vintners, Compton, Berkshire 01635 579 327
chv@saqnet.co.uk **MC**

Clifton Cellars, Bristol 0117 973 0287
clifton@cellars.freeserve.co.uk

Brian Coad Fine Wines, Plympton, Devon 01752 334970
  brian.coad@berkmann.co.uk ✪MC
Cockburns of Leith, Edinburgh 0131 346 1113
  sales@winelist.co.uk
Colombier Vins Fins, Swadlincote, Derbyshire
  01283 552552 colombier@colombierwines.co.uk MC
Compendium, Belfast 028 9079 1197
  info@compendiumwines.com
Connolly's, Birmingham 0121 236 9269
  chris@connollyswine.co.uk ✪
Constantine Stores, Falmouth, Cornwall 01326 340226
  andrew@drinkfinder.co.uk
Cooden Cellars, Eastbourne, East Sussex 01323 649663
  cooden@lineone.net ✪
Corks, Cotham, Bristol 0117 973 1620
  sales@corksof.com
Corkscrew Wines, Carlisle, Cumbria 01228 543033
  corkscrewwines@aol.com
Corney & Barrow, London 020 7265 2400
  wine@corbar.co.uk ✪F
Crane River Fine Wines, Middlesex 020 8891 4343
  craneriviera@aol.com MC
Creber's, Tavistock, Devon 01822 612266
Croque-en-Bouche, Malvern Wells, Worcestershire
  01684 565612 mail@croque.co.uk ✪MC

Dartmouth Vintners, Dartmouth, Devon 01803 832602
  bill@dartmouthvintners.fsnet.co.uk
Andrew Darwin Fine Wines, Kington, Herefordshire
  01544 230534 darwin@kc3.co.uk
Davy's Wine Merchants, London 020 7407 9670
  jdavy@davy.co.uk
Decorum Vintners, London 020 8969 6581
  admin@decvin.com ✪MC

deFINE Food and Wine, Sandiway, Cheshire 01606 882101
office@definefoodandwine.com ○
Rodney Densem Wines, Crewe 01270 212200
sales@rdwines.com
F.L. Dickins, Rickmansworth, Hertfordshire
01923 773636
Direct Wine Shipments, Belfast 028 9050 8000
enquiry@directwine.co.uk ○
Direct Wines, Theale, Reading 0870 444 8383
orders@laithwaites.co.uk **MF**
Dodici Wines, Harpenden, Hertfordshire 01582 713004
info@dodici.co.uk
Domaine Direct, London 020 7837 1142
mail@domainedirect.co.uk ○**C**
The Dorchester Wine Centre at Eldridge Pope, Dorchester,
Dorset 01305 258266 wineshopdorchester@
eldridge.pope.co.uk ○
Dunells Premier Wines Ltd, St Peter, Jersey 01534 736418
dunells.wines@jerseymail.co.uk ○

Eagle's Wines, London 020 7223 7209
East Coast Wines, Grimsby, South Humberside
01472 827207 sales@eastcoastwinewarehouse.com
Edencroft Fine Wines, Nantwich, Cheshire 01270 629975
sales@edencroft.co.uk
Ells Fine Wines, Portadown 028 3833 2306
rrwines@hotmail.com
El Vino, London 020 7353 5384 all@elvino.co.uk
English Wine Centre, Alfriston Roundabout, East Sussex
01323 870164 bottles@englishwine.co.uk
Eton Vintners, Windsor 01753 790188
sales@etonvintners.co.uk **M**
Evertons, Abberley, Worcestershire 01299 890113
sales@evertonswines.co.uk

Evingtons Wine Merchants, Leicester 0116 254 2702
evingtonwine@fsbdial.co.uk
Execellars, Kennford, Exeter, Devon 0800 0838075
andy@execellars.co.uk

Farr Vintners, London 020 7821 2000
sales@farrvintners.com ✪MF
Fine & Rare Wines, London 020 8960 1995
wine@frw.co.uk ✪MF
Fine Cheese Co., Bath 01225 483407 sales@finecheese.co.uk
Fine Wines of New Zealand, London 020 7482 0093
sales@fwnz.co.uk ✪M
Irma Fingal-Rock, Monmouth, Monmouthshire
01600 712372 tom@pinotnoir.co.uk
Flagship Wines, St Albans, Hertfordshire 01727 865309
info@flagshipwines.co.uk ✪
Le Fleming Wines, Harpenden, Hertfordshire
01582 760125 MC
Rodney Fletcher Vintners, Horsmonden, Kent
01892 723084 wine@rfvintners.co.uk
The Flying Corkscrew, Hemel Hempstead, Hertfordshire
01442 412311 sales@flyingcorkscrew.com ✪
La Forge Wines, Marksbury, Bath 01761 472349
kevin@laforgewines.com MF
Fortnum & Mason, London 020 7734 8040
info@fortnumandmason.co.uk ✪
Four Walls Wine Company, Chilgrove, West Sussex
01243 535360 fourwallswine@aol.com ✪MF
Friarwood, London 020 7736 2628 sales@friarwood.com
FWW Wines, London 020 8567 3731
sales@fwwwines.demon.co.uk ✪MC

Gallery Wines, Gomshall, Surrey 01483 203795
info@thegomshallgallery.net

Garland Wine Cellar, Ashtead, Surrey 01372 275247
stephen@garlandwines.co.uk

Garrards, Cockermouth, Cumbria 01900 823592
admin@garrards-wine.co.uk

Gauntleys, Nottingham 0115 911 0555
rhone@gauntleywine.com ✪

General Wine Company, Liphook, Hampshire
01428 727744 sales@thegeneralwine.co.uk ✪

Goedhuis & Co., London 020 7793 7900
sales@goedhuis.com ✪MCF

Gourmet Vintners, Billingshurst, West Sussex
01403 784128 sales@gourmetvintners.co.uk

Peter Graham Wines, Norwich, Norfolk 01603 625657
louisa@petergrahamwines.com

Richard Granger Fine Wine Merchants, Newcastle upon
Tyne 0191 281 5000 sales@richardgrangerwines.co.uk

The Grape Shop, London 020 7924 3638
dp@thegrapeshop.com ✪

The Great Grog Wine Co., Edinburgh 0131 662 4777
www.greatgrog.co.uk

Great Northern Wines, Ripon, North Yorkshire
01765 606767 info@greatnorthernwine.com M

Great Western Wine Company, Bath 01225 322800
post@greatwesternwine.co.uk ✪

Peter Green, Edinburgh 0131 229 5925
shop@petergreenwines.com

The Grogblossom, London 020 7794 7808

Patrick Grubb Selections, Oxford 01869 340229
patrickgrubbselections@btinternet.com ✪

Gunson Fine Wines, Hastings, East Sussex 01424 445777
dion@gfwl.co.uk ✪MC

H & H Bancroft, London 020 7232 5450
sales@handhbancroftwines.com ✪MC

Alexander Hadleigh, Locks Heath, Southampton
01489 885959 info@ahadleigh-wine.com

Hailsham Cellars, Hailsham, East Sussex 01323 441212
wine@hailshamcellars.com

Halifax Wine Company, Halifax, West Yorkshire
01422 256333 andy@halifaxwinecompany.com

Hall & Woodhouse Ltd, Blandford, Dorset 01258 452 141
admin@hall-woodhouse.co.uk

Handford Wines, London 020 7221 9614
wine@handford.net ✪F

Hanslope Wines, Milton Keynes, Buckinghamshire
01908 510262 charles@hanslopewines.co.uk

Roger Harris Wines, Weston Longville, Norfolk
01603 880171 sales@rogerharriswines.co.uk ✪MC

Harrods, London 020 7730 1234 ✪F

Harrogate Fine Wine, Harrogate, North Yorkshire
01423 522270 enquiries@harrogatefinewine.co.uk

Harvey Nichols & Co., London 020 7201 8537
wineshop@harveynichols.com ✪

Richard Harvey Wines, Wareham, Dorset 01929 481437
harvey@lds.co.uk MC

The Haslemere Cellar, Haslemere, Surrey 01428 645081
info@haslemerecellar.co.uk ✪

Hayman Barwell Jones, Ipswich, Suffolk
01473 232322 ✪MC

Haynes, Hanson & Clark, London 020 7259 0102
london@hhandc.co.uk and Stow-on-the-Wold,
Gloucestershire 01451 870808 stow@hhandc.co.uk ✪

Hedley Wright, Bishop's Stortford, Hertfordshire
01279 465818 sales@hedleywright.co.uk C

Pierre Henck, Walsall, West Midlands 01543 377 111
birm1@morgenrot.co.uk MC

Henderson Wines, Edinburgh 0131 447 8580
hendersonwines@btconnect.com

Charles Hennings Vintners, Pulborough, West Sussex
01798 872671 sales@chv-wine.co.uk

Hicks & Don, Edington, Wiltshire 01380 831234
mailbox@hicksanddon.co.uk **M**

George Hill, Loughborough, Leicestershire 01509 212717
andrewh@georgehill.co.uk

Hills Drinks and Oasis Wines, Benfleet, Essex 01268 772611
hillsdrinks@btconnect.com

Hopton Wines, Kidderminster, Shropshire 01299 270734
chris@hoptoncourt.fsnet.co.uk **MC**

Hoults Wine Merchants, Huddersfield, West Yorkshire
01484 510700 rob@hoults-winemerchants.co.uk

House of Townend, Kingston upon Hull, East Yorkshire
01482 586582 info@houseoftownend.co.uk ✪

Ian G. Howe, Newark, Nottinghamshire 01636 704366
howe@chablis-burgundy.co.uk

Victor Hugo Wines, St Saviour, Jersey 01534 507977
sales@victor-hugo-wines.com

Inspired Wines, Cleobury Mortimer, Shropshire
01299 270064 sales@inspired-wines.co.uk

Inverarity Vaults, Biggar 01899 308000
info@inverarity-vaults.com

Irvine Robertson, Edinburgh 0131 553 3521
irviner@nildram.co.uk **C**

Jeroboams (incorporating **Laytons Wine Merchants**),
London 020 7259 6716 sales@jeroboams.co.uk ✪

Michael Jobling, Newcastle-upon-Tyne 0191 378 4554
mjwines@btconnect.com **MC**

N.D. John, Swansea 01792 644688
nj@ndjohnwinemerchants.co.uk

The Jolly Vintner, Tiverton, Devon
01884 255644

L & F Jones, Radstock near Bath 01761 417117
buying.buying@lfjones.aclm.co.uk
S.H. Jones, Banbury, Oxfordshire 01295 251179
shj@shjones.com ✪
Justerini & Brooks, London 020 7484 6400 ✪F
Just in Case Wine Merchants, Bishop's Waltham,
Hampshire 01489 892969
justincase@bishopswaltham9.fsnet.co.uk

Joseph Keegan & Sons Ltd, Holyhead, Isle of Anglesey
01407 762333 enquiries@josephkeegan.co.uk
Christopher Keiller, Redruth, Cornwall 01209 215706
ghost@gladys.demon.co.uk
John Kelly Wines, Boston Spa, West Yorkshire
01937 842965 john@kellywines.co.uk **MC**
Kelly of Cults Ltd, Aberdeen 0845 456 1902
Kendalls, Manchester 0161 8323414
Kendrick Wines, Bromley, Kent 020 8467 7524
kmcclem@aol.com
David Kibble Wines, Fontwell, West Sussex
01243 544111
Richard Kihl, Aldeburgh, Suffolk 01728 454455
sales@richardkihl.ltd.uk ✪CF

Laithwaites, Reading, Berkshire 0870 444 8282
orders@laithwaites.co.uk **MC**
Lay & Wheeler, Holton St Mary, Suffolk 0845 330 1855
sales@laywheeler.com ✪
Laymont & Shaw, Truro, Cornwall 01872 270545
info@laymont-shaw.co.uk ✪MC
Lea & Sandeman, London 020 7244 0522
sales@leaandsandeman.co.uk ✪
Liberty Wine, London 020 7720 5350
into@libertywine.co.uk ✪MC

O.W. Loeb & Co. Ltd, London 020 7234 0385
finewine@owloeb.com ✪MC
J & H Logan, Edinburgh 0131 667 2855
Longford Wines, Lewes, East Sussex 01273 400012
longfordwines@aol.com MC
Love Saves the Day, Manchester 0161 832 0777
chris@lovesavestheday.co.uk ✪
Luckins Wine Store, Great Dunmow, Essex 01371 872839
andyfiltness@winebuffs.net
Luvian's Bottle Shop, Cupar, Fife 01334 654820
info@luvians.com

Magnum Wine Company, Swindon, Wiltshire
01793 642569 ✪
Map Wines, Bridgwater, Somerset 01278 459 622
davidpreece@map-wines.freeserve.co.uk
Martinez Wines, Ilkley, West Yorkshire 01943 603241
editor@martinez.co.uk ✪MC
Mason & Mason, West Stoke, West Sussex 01243 535364
sales@masonandmasonwines.co.uk ✪MC
Mayfair Cellars, London 020 7386 7999
sales@mayfaircellars.co.uk MC
Mill Hill Wines, London 020 8959 6754
laurence@millhillwines.com
Mille Gusti, London 020 8997 3932 millegusti@
hotmail.com ✪MC
Mills Whitcombe, Peterchurch, Herefordshire
01981 550028 info@millswhitcombe.co.uk ✪C
Milton Sandford Wines, Knowl Hill, Berkshire
01628 829449 sales@miltonsandfordwines.com ✪MC
Mitchells Wines, Sheffield 0114 274 5587
info@mitchellsdirect.com
Montrachet Fine Wines, London 020 7928 1990
charles@montrachetwine.com ✪MC

Moonshine, Bourne, Lincolnshire 01778 421050
andy@moonshine.fsbusiness.co.uk
Moreno Wines, London 020 7286 0678 sales@
moreno-wines.co.uk ✪
Moriarty Vintners, Cardiff 029 2022 9996
sales@moriarty-vintners.com

Nectarous Wines, Cheltenham, Gloucestershire
01242 224466 taste@nectarous.co.uk
The New Pantry, London 020 7602 6964
James Nicholson, Crossgar, Co. Down, Northern Ireland
028 4483 0091 shop@jnwine.com ✪
Nickolls & Perks, Stourbridge, West Midlands
01384 394518 sales@nickollsandperks.co.uk
Nicolas UK of London 20+ stores 020 8944 7514
www.nicolas.co.uk
Nidderdale Fine Wines, Harrogate, North Yorkshire
01423 711703 info@southaustralianwines.com ✪
Noble Rot Wine Warehouse, Bromsgrove, Worcestershire
01527 575606 sales@noble-rot.co.uk ✪
The Nobody Inn, Doddiscombsleigh, Devon 01647 252394
info@nobodyinn.co.uk ✪
Novum Wines, London 020 7820 6720
info@novumwines.com ✪

Off the Vine, St Albans, Hertfordshire 01727 898290
The Old Forge Wine Cellar, Storrington, West Sussex
01903 744246 chris@worldofwine.co.uk
Oxford Wine Company, Witney, Oxfordshire 01865 301144
info@oxfordwine.co.uk ✪
Oz Wines, London 0845 450 1261 sales@ozwines.co.uk ✪

Page & Sons, Ramsgate, Kent 01843 591214
mail@pageandsons.co.uk

Thomas Panton, Tetbury, Gloucestershire 01666 503088
info@wineimporter.co.uk M

Parfrements, Coventry, West Midlands 024 7650 3646

Paxton & Whitfield, London 020 7930 0259
sales@cheesemongers.co.uk

Peake Wine Associates, Fareham, Hampshire 01329 822733
roy@farehamwinecellar.co.uk

Thos Peatling, Bury St Edmunds, Suffolk 01284 714285
sales@thospeatling.co.uk

Peckham & Rye, Glasgow 0141 445 4555
alan.rose@peckhams.co.uk ❂

Penistone Court Wine Cellars, Penistone, Sheffield
01226 766037 pcwc@dircon.co.uk ❂MC

Philglas & Swiggot, London 020 7924 4494
wine@philglas-swiggot.co.uk ❂

Laurence Philippe Wines, Chelmsford, Essex 01245 475454
lpwines@lineone.net

Christopher Piper Wines, Ottery St Mary,
Devon 01404 814139 sales@
christopherpiperwines.co.uk ❂

Plato Harrison, Kirkby Lonsdale, Cumbria 01524 271288
info@platoharrison.com

Terry Platt Wine Merchants, Llandudno, Conwy
01492 874099 info@terryplattwines.co.uk ❂MC

Planet Wine Ltd, Sale, Cheshire 0161 973 1122
sales@planetwine.co.uk MC

Playford Ros, Sowerby, North Yorkshire 01845 526777
sales@playfordros.com MC

Portal, Dingwall & Norris, Emsworth, Hampshire
01243 370280 philip@pdnagencies.com

Portland Wine Co., Sale, Manchester 0161 962 8752
portwineco@aol.com

Premier Cru Fine Wine, Guiseley, Leeds 01943 877004
enquiries@premiercrufinewine.co.uk

Quay West Wines, Stoke Canon, Exeter 01392 841833
sales@quaywestwines.co.uk **C**
Quellyn Roberts, Chester, Cheshire 01244 310455
sales@qrwines.co.uk

R.S. Wines, Winford, Bath and Northeast Somerset
01275 331 444 sales@rswines.co.uk **MC**
Arthur Rackham Emporia, Guildford, Surrey
0870 870 1110 **C**
Raeburn Fine Wines, Edinburgh 0131 343 1159
sales@raeburnfinewines.com ✪
Ravensbourne Wine, London 020 8692 9655
sales@ravensbournewine.co.uk **C**
Regency Wines, Exeter, Devon 01392 444123
Reid Wines, Hallatrow, Bristol 01761 452645
reidwines@aol.com ✪MF
Revelstoke Wines, London 020 8545 0077
sales@revelstoke.co.uk ✪MC
Richardson & Sons, Whitehaven, Cumbria 01946 65334
richardsonandsons@btconnect.com
Howard Ripley Ltd, London 020 8877 3065
info@howardripley.com ✪MC
Roberson, London 020 7371 2121 retail@roberson.co.uk ✪
Roberts & Speight, Beverley, East Yorkshire 01482 870717
sales@foodbites.karoo.co.uk
Robert Rolls, London 020 7606 1166 mail@rollswine.com
✪MCF
R & R Fine Wines, Bury, Lancashire 0161 762 0022
fine.wines@btconnect.com ✪

St Martin Vintners, Brighton, East Sussex 01273 777788
sales@stmartinvintners.co.uk
Sandhams Wine Merchants Ltd, Caistor, Lincolnshire
01472 852118 sales@sandhamswine.co.uk

Scatchard, Liverpool 0151 236 6468
jon@scatchard.com

Seckford Wines, Woodbridge, Suffolk 01394 446622
sales@seckfordwines.co.uk ✪MCF

Selfridges, London 020 7318 3730 and Manchester
0161 838 0659 wine.club@selfridges.co.uk ✪

Shaftesbury Fine Wines, Shaftesbury, Dorset
01747 850059 prbennett@shafwine.fsnet.co.uk

Shaws of Beaumaris, Isle of Anglesey 01248 810328
wines@shaws.sagehost.co.uk

Edward Sheldon, Shipston-on-Stour, Warwickshire
01608 661409 finewine@edward-sheldon.co.uk

H. Smith, Ashbourne, Derbyshire 01335 342150
horace.smith@tiscali.co.uk

Laurence Smith, Edinburgh 0131 667 3327
vintnersmith@aol.com **MC**

Soho Wine Supply, London 020 7636 8490
info@sohowine.co.uk

Sommelier Wine Co. Ltd, St Peter Port, Guernsey
01481 721677 ✪

Springfield Wines, near Huddersfield, West Yorkshire
01484 864929 springfieldwines@aol.com

Frank Stainton Wines, Kendal, Cumbria 01539 731886
admin@stainton-wines.co.uk

Stanton Wine Co., Broadway, Worcestershire
01386 852501 sales@stantonwineco.co.uk

William Stedman, Caerleon, Newport 01633 430055
info@wmstedman.co.uk

Charles Steevenson, Tavistock, Devon 01822 616272
sales@steevensonwines.co.uk **MC**

Stevens Garnier, Oxford 01865 263303
info@stevensgarnier.co.uk ✪

Stokes Fine Wines, London 020 8944 5979
sales@stokesfinewines.com ✪MC

M = Mail order company, usually with no retail premises
F = Fine wine sales/wine broker/good range of expensive stuff!

Stone, Vine & Sun, Winchester, Hampshire 0845 061 4604
sales@stonevine.co.uk ✪

Stratford's Wine Agencies, Cookham-on-Thames,
Berkshire 01628 810606 sales@stratfordwine.co.uk ✪MC

The Sussex Wine Company, Eastbourne, East Sussex
01323 431143 sales@thesussexwinecompany.co.uk ✪

SWIG, London 020 8995 7060
imbibe@swig.co.uk ✪MC

T & W Wines, Brandon, Suffolk 01842 814414
contact@tw-wines.com

Tanners, Shrewsbury, Shropshire 01743 234455
sales@tanners-wines.co.uk ✪

Taurus Wines, Bramley, Surrey 01483 548484
sales@tauruswines.co.uk

ten-acre wines, Welwyn Garden City, Hertfordshire
01707 372760 brian@ten-acre.com ✪

Terroir, Skipton, North Yorkshire 01756 700512
enquiries@terroirlanguedoc.co.uk ✪MC

Theatre of Wine, London 020 8858 6363

Totnes Wine Co., Totnes, Devon 01803 866357
info@totneswine.co.uk

Trenchermans, Sherborne, Dorset 01935 432857
info@trenchermans.com

Turville Valley Wines, Great Missenden, Buckinghamshire
01494 868818 info@turville-valley-wines.com ✪MCF

Uncorked, London 020 7638 5998 drink@uncorked.co.uk ✪

Unwined Ltd, Sedgebrook, Nottinghamshire
01949 844324 enquiries@unwined.biz

Valvona & Crolla, Edinburgh 0131 556 6066
sales@valvonacrolla.co.uk ✪

Helen Verdcourt, Maidenhead, Berkshire 01628 625577 MC

Veritas Wines, Cambridge 01223 212500
info@veritaswines.co.uk

Vicki's Wine Merchants, Chobham, Surrey
01276 858374

Les Vignerons de St Georges, Windlesham, Surrey 01276
850136 gratfood@the-inn.co.uk

Villeneuve Wines, Peebles, Haddington and Edinburgh
01721 722500 wines@villeneuvewines.com ✪

Vin du Van, Appledore, Kent 01233 758727 ✪MC

Vinceremos, Leeds 0113 244 0002 info@vinceremos.co.uk
MC

The Vine Trail, Hotwells, Bristol 0117 921 1770
enquiries@vinetrail.co.uk ✪MC

The Vineyard, Dorking, Surrey 01306 876828
jh@vineyard-direct.co.uk

The Vineyard Cellars, Hungerford, Berkshire 01488 681313
jameshocking@vineyardcellars.com ✪MC

Vino Vino, New Malden, Surrey 07703 436949
vinovino@macunlimited.net MC

The Vintage House, London 020 7437 2592
vintagehouse.co@virgin.net

Vintage Roots, Arborfield, Berkshire 0118 976 1999
info@vintageroots.co.uk ✪M

Vintage Wine Cellars, Luton, Bedfordshire 01582 455068
sales@vintagewinecellars.co.uk

Wadebridge Wines, Wadebridge, Cornwall 01208 812692
enquiries@wwrw.co.uk

Waterloo Wine, London 020 7403 7967
sales@waterloowine.co.uk

Waters of Coventry, Heathcote, Warwick 01926 888889
info@waters-wine-merchants.co.uk

T.B. Watson Ltd, Dumfries, Dumfriesshire 01387 256601
karen@tbwatson.co.uk

David J. Watt Fine Wines, Ashby-de-la-Zouch,
Leicestershire 01530 413953 fwatt@lineone.net **M**

Wattisfield Wines, Bury St Edmunds, Suffolk 01359 251260

Weavers of Nottingham, Nottingham 0115 958 0922
weavers@weaverswines.com ✪

Welshpool Wine, Powys 01938 553243
info@welshpoolwine.com ✪

Wessex Wines, Bridport, Dorset 01308 427177
wessexwines@amserve.com **C**

Whitebridge Wines, Stone, Staffordshire 01785 817229
sales@whitebridgewines.co.uk

Whitesides, Clitheroe, Lancashire 01200 422281
whitesides.wine@btconnect.com

Whittalls Wines, Walsall, West Midlands 01922 636161
jrushton@efb.co.uk **C**

Wicked Wines, Pockthorpe, Kilham, East Yorkshire
01377 255725

Wilkinson Vintners Ltd, London 020 7616 0404
wine@wilkinsonvintners.com ✪**MCF**

James Williams, Narberth, Pembrokeshire 01834 862200

Wimbledon Wine Cellar, London 020 8540 9979
enquiries@wimbledonwinecellar.com ✪

Winchcombe Wine Merchants, Winchcombe,
Gloucestershire 01451 850686

The WineBarn, Dummer, Hampshire 01256 391211
info@thewinebarn.co.uk ✪

Wine Barrels, London 020 7228 3306
edwood@scvintners.f9.co.uk

The Wine Cellar, South Croydon, Surrey 020 8657 6936
winecellarsnd@aol.com

Wine in Cornwall, Falmouth/Penryn, Cornwall 01326
379426 sales@wineincornwall.co.uk

The Wine Library, London 020 7481 0415
wine.library@virgin.net

The Wine Man, Streatley-on-Thames, West Berkshire
01635 203050 sales@wine-man.com MC

The Wine Mill, Nelson, Lancashire 01282 614618
enquiries@thewinemill.co.uk ✪

Wine Society, Stevenage, Hertfordshire 01438 741177
memberservices@thewinesociety.com ✪MCF

The Wine Treasury, London 020 7793 9999
bottled@winetreasury.com ✪MC

The Winery, London 020 7286 6475
info@thewineryuk.com ✪F

Wines of Interest, Ipswich, Suffolk 0870 224 5640
sales@winesofinterest.co.uk

Wine Raks, Aberdeen 01224 311460 mike@wineraks.co.uk

The Winesmith, Peterborough, Cambridgeshire
01780 783102 cases@winesmith.co.uk

WineTime, Milnthorpe, Cumbria 01539 562030 MC

Worcester Wine Co., Worcestershire 01905 425588

T. Wright, Bolton, Greater Manchester 01204 697805
wayne.t.wright@fsmill.net

The Wright Wine Company, Skipton, North Yorkshire
01756 700886 www.wineandwhisky.co.uk ✪

Wrightson & Co. Wine Merchants, Manfield, Darlington
01325 374134 simon@wrightsonwines.co.uk MC

Wycombe Wines, High Wycombe, Buckinghamshire
01494 437228

Peter Wylie Fine Wines, Plymtree, Devon 01884 277555
peter@wylie-fine-wines.demon.co.uk ✪F

Yapp Brothers, Mere, Wiltshire 01747 860423
sales@yapp.co.uk ✪MC

Noel Young Wines, Trumpington, Cambridgeshire
01223 844744 admin@nywines.co.uk ✪ F

AUSTRALIA		
Margaret River, WA		2003 2002 2001 2000 1999 1997 1996 1995 1994 1992 1991
Barossa Valley, SA		2004 2003 2002 2001 1998 1997 1996 1994 1993 1992 1991 1990 1988 1986
Clare Valley, SA		2005 2004 2003 2002 2001 1999 1998 1997 1996 1994 1992 1991 1990
Coonawarra, SA		2003 2002 2001 2000 1999 1998 1996 1994 1993 1991 1990
Yarra Valley, VIC		2004 2003 2002 2001 1998 1997 1996 1994
Hunter Valley, NSW		2004 2003 2002 2000 1999 1998 1997 1995 1992 1991 1990

FRANCE		
Alsace		2004 2003 2002 2001 2000 1999 1998 1997 1996 1995 1993 1990 1989 1988 1986 1985 1983
Burgundy	Chablis	2004 2003 2002 2000 1999 1998 1997 1996 1995 1992 1990 1989 1988 1986
	Côte d'Or	2003 2002 2001 2000 1999 1998 1997 1996 1995 1992 1990 1989 1988 1986 1985 1983
	Beaujolais	2003 2002 2000 1999 1998 1997 1995 1990 1989 1988

Bordeaux	Left Bank	2003 2001 2000 1999 1998 1996 1995 1990 1989 1988 1986 1985 1983 1982
	Right Bank	2003 2001 2000 1999 1998 1996 1995 1990 1989 1988 1986 1985 1983 1982
	Sauternes	2003 2001 1999 1998 1997 1996 1995 1990 1989 1988 1986 1983

| Rhône | Northern | 2003 2001 2000 1999 1998 1997 1996 1995 1994 1990 1989 1988 1985 1983 |
| | Southern | 2003 2001 2000 1999 1998 1995 1990 1989 1988 1985 1983 |

| Loire | Sweeties | 2003 2002 2001 2000 1999 1997 1996 1995 1993 1990 1989 1988 1985 1983 1982 |

| Champagne | | 2003 2002 2000 1998 1997 1996 1995 1990 1989 1988 1985 1980 1976 |

| Languedoc/ Roussillon | | 2003 2001 2000 1999 1998 1996 1995 1994 1993 1990 1989 1988 1986 1985 |

| Provence | | 2003 2001 2000 1999 1998 1997 1996 1995 1993 1991 1990 1989 1988 1985 |

GERMANY

| Mosel | | 2004 2003 2002 2001 1999 1997 1996 1995 1994 1993 1992 1990 1989 1988 1983 |

| Rheingau | | 2004 2003 2002 2001 1999 1997 1996 1995 1994 1993 1992 1990 1989 1988 1983 |

ITALY

Piedmont	2003 2001 2000 1998 1997 1996 1990 1989 1988 1985
Tuscany	2003 2001 1999 1997 1995 1993 1990 1988 1985 1983 1982
Veneto	2003 2001 2000 1997 1995 1993 1990 1988 1985

NEW ZEALAND

North Island Hawkes Bay, (reds)	2003 2002 2001 2000 1999 1998 1994 1991 1990
South Island Marlborough, (whites)	2005 2004 2003 2002 2001 2000 1999 1998

PORTUGAL

Vintage Port	2003 2000 1997 1995 1994 1992 1991 1985 1983 1977 1970 1966 1963

SOUTH AFRICA

	2003 2002 2001 2000 1999 1998 1997 1995

SOUTH AMERICA

Chile	2004 2003 2002 2001 1999 1996 1995
Argentina	2004 2002 2001 1999 1997 1996 1995

SPAIN	
Rioja	2004 2003 2002 2001 2000 1999 1998 1996 1995 1994 1991 1990 1987 1982 1981
Ribera del Duero	2003 2001 1999 1998 1996 1995 1994 1990 1987 1986 1983 1982 1981
Penedès/Priorat	2003 2001 2000 1999 1998 1996 1995 1994 1993 1992 1985

USA	
North Coast	2003 2002 2001 1999 1998 1997 1996 1995 1994 1992 1991 1990
Napa and Carneros	2003 2002 2001 1999 1997 1995 1994 1992 1991 1990 1987 1986 1985 1984
Central Coast	2003 2002 2001 1999 1998 1997 1996 1995 1994 1993 1992 1991 1990
Oregon/Washington	2003 2002 2001 2000 1999 1998 1996 1994 1992 1990 1989

INDEX BY RETAILER

INDEX BY WINE

ACKNOWLEDGEMENTS

I would like to extend my heartfelt thanks to every single person in the UK wine trade and to all of those wonderful people abroad who have helped me so much in my job over the past twelve months. I have travelled extensively, tasted more wines than ever and have learned so much more about the amazing world of wine. The industry moves frighteningly quickly, with new and incredible wines emerging every day. Your collective encouragement is phenomenal – I simply couldn't write this book without you. *The Wine List* is an amazing book to work on and I look forward to doing it all again next year. Special thanks must go to Nathalie, Isadora, Elspeth, Ma and Pa for their huge support. I would also like to thank Robert Kirby, my agent, and the team at Headline – Bryone, Emily, Fiona, George, James, Kerr, Nicci, Pippa, Simon, Val and especially my editor Jo Roberts-Miller – she has an uncanny knack for making this all seem easy on the surface when in reality it is brain-sapping, ball-busting and breakdown-inducing. Somehow she gets me through and I always emerge with a smile on my face when I finally get a copy of the finished book in my hand. Thank you all.

If you are a wine merchant in the UK and would like to be mentioned in this list, or if your details are listed incorrectly, the author and publisher will be delighted to amend later editions.

Write to The Wine List, c/o Headline Book Publishing, 338 Euston Road, London, NW1 3BH.

TABLE OF ABBREVIATIONS

Asd	Asda
Boo	E. H. Booth & Co
Bot	Bottoms Up
Coo	Co-operative Group (CWS)
M&S	Marks & Spencer
Maj	Majestic Wine Warehouses
Mor	Wm Morrison
Odd	Oddbins
OFW	Oddbins Fine Wine
Sai	Sainsbury's
Som	Somerfield Stores
Tes	Tesco Stores
Thr	Thresher
Unw	Unwins Ltd
Wai	Waitrose
WCe	Wine Cellar
WRa	Wine Rack